State College

at

Framingham

LANDS
BEYOND THE FOREST

LANDS

BEYOND THE FOREST

by PAUL B. SEARS

Illustrations by STANLEY WYATT

PRENTICE-HALL, Inc., Englewood Cliffs, N.J.

LANDS BEYOND THE FOREST
by Paul B. Sears
© 1969 by Paul B. Sears

Library of Congress Catalog Card Number: 68-8126

Printed in the United States of America · T

Prentice-Hall International, Inc., London
Prentice-Hall of Australia, Pty. Ltd., Sydney
Prentice-Hall of Canada, Ltd., Toronto
Prentice-Hall of India Private Ltd., New Delhi
Prentice-Hall of Japan, Inc., Tokyo

Unless otherwise credited, photos by Paul B. Sears.

Acknowledgment is made for permission to reprint excerpts
from the following works:

THE BERNAL DIAZ CHRONICLE, translated by Albert Idell, Editor.
Copyright © 1965 by Albert Idell. Reprinted by permission
of Doubleday & Company, Inc.

MY ANTONIA, by Willa Cather, reprinted by permission of the
publisher, Houghton Mifflin Company.

Acknowledgments

Among the many to whom I owe thanks I am especially grateful to:
Kenneth Bechtel and the Belvedere Foundation for substantial assistance,
including opportunities to study the classical desert of Baja California; to
Nancy Bechtel, James Blackman and Oliver Milton for generously furnish-
ing photographs; to Doubleday for permission to quote from Idell's translation
of the *Bernal Díaz Chronicle* and to Houghton Mifflin for permission to quote
from Willa Cather's *My Antonia;* to Edna Papazian for invaluable help
in checking references and copying manuscript; and finally to my wife Marjorie
L. Sears for skilled criticism seasoned with constant encouragement.

Books by Paul B. Sears

Deserts on the March
This Is Our World
Life and Environment
Who Are These Americans?
Charles Darwin
The Living Landscape
Lands Beyond the Forest

Contents

Introduction

TO most Americans, both urban and suburban, grass is merely a minor status symbol indispensable to lawns and golf. To keep it mowed and free of dandelion requires a great deal of labor—personal or delegated. An ill-kept lawn degrades the owner, and no lawn at all makes him déclassé.

That sour economist Thorstein Veblen insisted that property owners cultivated lawns in order to demonstrate that they were prosperous enough to afford "conspicuous expenditure." The lawn, he wrote, proclaimed that its owner could afford to waste a plot of ground that could otherwise have raised vegetables. In this book Professor Sears suggests a less disagreeable theory: perhaps by surrounding ourselves with grass we symbolically acknowledge its role in the rise of civilization.

Whether or not lawn-owners are aware of the fact, grass has been one of the determining factors in mankind's multi-million-year history. One of nature's most fateful inventions for man was the seed-bearing grasses; no spore-bearing plant could have been widely cultivated. Only seed-bearing grasses could produce bread, and only open country could support grass enough to nourish the beasts which man tamed and slaughtered.

Professor Sears' fascinating book can be considered a companion volume to Rutherford Platt's *The Great American Forest:* Out of the five regions explored by man—the deserts, the mountains, the seas, the forest and the grasslands—the last two have been the most important. Man, no doubt, was first a forest dweller and became a settled agriculturist only after climatic changes had provided the open prairies where a different flora and fauna could thrive.

But Professor Sears' book is a personal and poetic discussion as well as a scientific one. For most of his life, he has lived in a region where grasslands were a primary fact of the landscape and of life. He has for open spaces a feeling of personal involvement, which no man who was merely an observer could possess. He has written what is, in part, an act of piety that pays tribute to the botanical, ecological, and historic significance of the grasslands. His book is an imaginative and aesthetic, as well as an informative, experience.

At present, there is considerable difference of opinion among biologists over the future of the life sciences. To many, recent advances in the biochemistry of the cell have rendered our older knowledge obsolete, or at best, irrelevant. Others have warned that to retreat into the ultramicroscopic world is to turn our backs on the most significant aspects of life and living organisms. Natural history represents the approach furthest removed from pure biochemistry, and Professor Sears is an ecologist—a student of the most modern form of natural history. His book is a moving rebuttal to those who may say that natural history is dead.

—Joseph Wood Krutch

LANDS
BEYOND THE FOREST

chapter one

A Growing Enchantment

ALCOHOL, we are told with some truth, is likely to have an enhanced attraction for people reared on total abstinence. Something of the sort may explain my lifelong interest in the prairies and other treeless areas. I grew up in northern Ohio where, even after a century of dogged cutting, trees were never out of sight.

In whatever direction one looked over this fair and gently rolling land there were trees, often groves of them, within the horizon. Roads and railroads were in many places still shaded by woodland on both sides. It was tantalizing to learn that there were great reaches of the earth where no trees grew. It was difficult even to envision such places. Much the same was true of mountains, then and for a long time afterwards to come outside my range of experience.

Open water—not the salty ocean but the sweet-water inland sea fifty miles to the north—was the first of the broad open faces of nature to take on reality to a then five-year-old. As the train pulled slowly alongside the water's edge there came into view a thicket of masts, interrupted here and there by a white wooden sidewheeler. At that time there were still many sailing vessels bringing down white pine lumber from Michigan, Wisconsin, and Minnesota and carrying back coal.

Beyond this unfamiliar array stretched a vast gray-green sheet dappled and dancing in a light breeze. The impression of it, after seventy years, remains in the realm of sensation, not to be translated adequately into words.

Knowledge of mountain and desert came to us more or less casually through spoken word and printed page. Of the existence of the great interior grasslands with their open sky and teeming life we had direct testimony, quite as convincing as that which the good Mrs. Temple gave us of the All-Seeing Eye each Sunday morning.

Our father had completed his formal education by graduation from high school in 1878. This was toward the close of the bloody decade which had virtually wiped out the bison and quieted the Indians, opening the prairies and plains to settlement.

Father's maternal uncles had settled along the Missouri in southeastern Nebraska after doffing their blue uniforms in 1865. Quite reasonably, in view of the great surge westward then going on, Father joined cousins of his own age in a wagon trip across the prairies. The landscape, now freed of its larger native fauna, human and bovine, was otherwise still much as it had been. The covered wagon was drawn by a span of mules. The way was open in all directions; one could easily take off across the open prairie with his team and wagon from whatever roads there were.

So it came about that we were told of a western land of grasses and flowers, with no trees save for the fringes of woods down in the valleys close to the riversides. There was still an abundance of dried buffalo "chips" for fuel. There were howling coyotes at night. Prairie chickens. Prairie dogs. Tiny owls. Jackrabbits and rattlesnakes. With prairie chicken on the uplands and squirrel and cottontail in the narrow gallery forests bordering the rivers, it was almost possible to live off the country.

We never tired of hearing, from the wagon seat, how these young explorers would shoot jackrabbits by firing "between the ears of the mules," and we were solemnly assured that only the mules had ears bigger than those of the jackrabbits. (I think the sober deportment of these Nebraska mules must have impressed Father, for he bore the scars of a previous adventure with a wild team that had run away with him and smashed a tollgate when he was in his early teens.)

Braided stream, characteristic of mountain streams debouching in semi-arid level landscape, the Grand Tetons.

Best of all were the accounts of the prairie dog towns, monitored by their little builders sitting erect on the ring of earth surrounding each burrow opening. Associated with them were elfin owls the size of house sparrows, and rattlesnakes, both given to spending much time underground.

As to the social arrangements in these villages, there were two schools of thought. One held that this weird assortment of creatures were tenants in common, dwelling together in a kind of idyllic *Pax Naturae*. The other—to which our mentor, a born skeptic, belonged—had little faith in any treaty involving the rattlesnake. Instead he looked upon the prairie dog as pioneer and excavator whose tunnels, however they came to be vacated, were taken over by others, quite as the mansions along Euclid Avenue in Cleveland were becoming shops, offices, and tenements.

The bison, of course, had by this time been slaughtered almost to the point of extinction. But the memory of these shaggy beasts was still fresh. Even two decades later one saw an occasional buffalo robe in carriage or cutter. A dashing physician whose outfit was in keeping with the fine horses he drove had a huge pair of gauntlets he wore in winter; these had been fashioned from the heavy pelt of the bison. Until they suddenly vanished from the market a good buffalo robe could be had for five dollars. I recall hearing that only a fool would pay more.

Later, as I began to read and explore for myself, I found that only a generation or two earlier there had been natural grasslands very close to our home. In fact the pasture at the edge of town where we took our cows each morning—less than a quarter mile away—lay at the head of one of these former prairies. The spring from which the cattle drank was a source of the Scioto River. Gathering volume as it flowed south, this stream traversed some eighteen miles of the "Plains," joining the Olentangy near Columbus and emptying finally into the Ohio.

Lying between two moraines the "Plains" were not, like the prairies farther west, an unbroken grassland. Instead they were dotted with slight rounded elevations that were wooded. These woods unlike most in the state contained neither beech nor sugar maple. Instead they bore oaks and hickories, fringed with sumac, wild rose, plum, and grape— all, as I learned much later, characteristic of the prairie border farther west.

It took some years for me to realize that these Plains had any relation to the western prairies whose description had so fascinated me. By 1890 the rich black soil that lay between the scattered oak-hickory groves had been drained and plowed or turned into pastures of tame grasses. Only along the roads and railroads and in an occasional odd corner were there remnants of the wild grasses—Big and Little Blue Stems, Indian and Panic Grasses, mixed with sunflowers, asters, goldenrods, rosinweed, and the lovely purple Blazing Star, all legitimate members of prairie communities.

Of the prairie animals there were few survivors. So far as is known, the last bison to be seen in Ohio were sighted by Christopher Gist in 1735. But a neighbor who had a farm some miles southwest of town told of picking up a rattlesnake now and then with a forkful of wild grass which was still being mowed. Many years later I learned from my entomologist friends that insects within these patches of Ohio prairie were, like the plants on which they depended, those whose normal home was some hundreds of miles farther west, in the great interior grasslands.

Meanwhile high school (with only a glimpse of botany) and college (with even less) were followed by two years study in that science in Nebraska, a prairie state. Under the guidance of a great teacher, the university there had turned out a remarkable number of professional botanists as well as lovers of plant life who were engaged in other occupations. This would seem like a fine achievement in line of duty in a state whose whole economy rested upon the plant kingdom. It was not so regarded everywhere. A Harvard professor lamented that the center of botanical influence had shifted from Harvard to the "barbarian schools of the Middle West."

Much of the original prairie in Nebraska had already been put to the plow. Fortunately, enough remained to give a sense of its texture, variety, and beauty. There was still some discussion in scientific circles as to why trees were scarce or lacking; fire, grazing, and soil each had its advocates. Among those who combined direct observation with common sense there was a verdict later confirmed by precise instrumental measurements: That the natural grasslands developed where the supply of available moisture was too meager to sustain forest.

Supporting this belief were the cloudless days of dry winter sunshine and the desiccating winds of spring, in contrast to the chilling dampness of the eastern cloud belts and the less violent air movement in the humid zones of forest. In a sense these were gauges provided by Nature. They registered no figures, it is true, but their meaning was clear enough, like that of perpetually dry skin and mucus. Someone put it in clear if

Treeless skyline in central Kansas.

somewhat inelegant fashion: "When I came out here I began to wonder why people kept fiddling with their noses. Now I know. They had to do it to breathe, by God."

The native plants and animals clearly reflected the fact that moisture was a major factor, or rather that the danger of drying out was a constant threat. Leaves were harsher and thicker than those of forest country, better shielded against sudden loss of water, as were the delicate tissues of growing points. Much of the drama of animal life went on underground during the heat of day and on the surface at night.

No calibrated meters were needed to prove that the grassland climate was continental in type, with sharp contrasts between day and night, winter and summer. One could shine with sweat during the day and shiver at night, be dew-soaked in early morning and dusty at noon. Weather records began with the establishment of army posts, but for a long time afterwards the nature of grassland climate and its effect upon vegetation was obscured. It is relatively easy to measure rainfall, but the figures taken alone can be misleading. Twenty inches of rainfall in Canada may support forest, but in Mexico are not enough to prevent desert. What was missing from the record and in many places still is only guessed at, was any measurement of evaporation. This is a difficult and involved matter, for it depends upon a number of quite variable circumstances such as wind, temperature, and the dryness of the air. Yet just as a budget is worthless without an estimate of income balanced against expenses, so the moisture available to support life in a given place must be estimated by balancing rainfall against evaporation. And just as financial budgets are based upon experience—that is, statements of past profit and loss—so must it be with water budgets for various habitats.

We have few measurements showing how much water, in inches per year, would be lost by evaporation if there were plenty of water for continuous evaporation. Still scarcer are figures on how much is actually lost from soil and other surfaces, including leaves, in any particular place. For the present we can do little better than observe that forest growth seems to depend upon an excess of available moisture over that lost by drying. Where moisture is inadequate to support trees there are low-growing grasses, herbs, and woody scrub. If there are tall plants, as in some deserts, these are widely spaced and capable of conserving water in various ways.

I returned to Ohio after two years in Nebraska, finding lively encouragement to study the vegetation of that state as it was when invaded and taken over by white men. I discovered that scattered through these forty thousand square miles of forest were many patches of grassland, aggregating between 5 and 10 percent of the area and occupying a number of different kinds of habitat. The explanation for these alien communities was to remain an intriguing problem for many years.

Meanwhile the exigencies of war interrupted other activities, placing me for some time at a military post on the edge of the Florida Everglades. Even here, in this lush subtropical environment, the paradox of treelessness persisted. The Glades themselves were a vast expanse of swamp, dominated by the wicked saw grass which is named for the sharp-toothed margins of its leaves. But scattered through this grassland were clumps of trees, either hammocks of live oak and palmetto or basins of cypress.

On the uplands, slightly higher than the Glades, there was a confusing mixture of pine woods, palmetto scrub, and—yes—prairies extensive enough to be supporting a livestock industry. Only when the rainy season came was it possible to make sense of this mélange of plant communities. From the air we saw that the prairies were regularly flooded, the palmetto scrub at the prairie's margin occasionally so, and the pine flatwoods not at all. Here then were prairies far outside the typical prairie climate, growing in broad shallow depressions whose occasional flooding favored grass rather than trees.

Shortly after this adventure I returned to the prairie province to remain there for nearly a score of years. There I found many opportunities to visit and traverse the zones of decreasing moisture, moving west from the subhumid tallgrass prairie across the mixture of tall and short grasses into the dry steppe or shortgrass country of the high plains which run north and south like a great carpet in front of the Rocky Mountains. It was this dry steppeland which during times of high prices for wheat had been exploited for that crop, and which gave us during the protracted drought and crop failures of the 1930's a graphic demonstration of the hazardous character of semiarid climate. Native plants have become adjusted through millennia to the vicissitudes of scant and highly variable water supply, surviving and holding the soil in place through thick and thin. Wheat, product of a remote region and long nurtured by man, lacks this background and is vulnerable. With the inevitable recurrence of drought, that autumn-planted crop fails to germinate. When spring winds arrive there is no vegetation to hold the looser soils in place, so that drifting and dust storms prevail. Such disaster is an unforgettable reminder that greedy and ignorant tampering with the landscape can be as dangerous as taking careless liberties with a cobra or a high-tension wire.

The activities of scientists are channeled, though some might hesitate to confess it, by what are essentially aesthetic and intuitive drives. One man pulls out his slide rule, another spends hours with his binoculars in a blind, a third manipulates an electron microscope. My interest was not limited to the vast grassland province west of the Mississippi. I was equally intrigued by the presence of authentic specimens of prairie east of that river. Particularly was this true of those in my native Ohio, where the present climate is favorable to forest growth.

Fortunately, the flowering plants that dominate earth's vegetation today often leave some record of their past distribution in the form of fossils. Especially useful are the tiny but very durable pollen grains that sift into lakes, ponds, and bogs and become embalmed in the bottom sediments there. Recovered, identified, and counted, these enable one to approximate the history of vegetation in the region. By methods that had been developed in Sweden, cores were taken from the material that had accumulated in wholly or partly filled Ohio lakes. These lakes, located in the general region where the scattered prairie outliers were present, had been formed after the retreat of the last great ice sheet. Samples from bottom to top of the cores, properly treated and examined by the microscope, revealed a stately succession of plant life beginning with forests of scattered spruce that grew in the cold wake of the retreating ice. Gradually more warmth-loving species returned from southern refuges and took over.

But the answer to my question came with the evidence that some 3500 years ago there was a maximum of warmth and dryness which for a time enabled prairie life from the West to extend well into the forest zone. The small prairie enclaves of Ohio and neighboring states were actually relics, surviving by dint of possession and favorable local conditions (not always clear) amidst the humid forest.

Living communities at the margins of the great climatic zones are in constant competition, with circumstances now favoring one, now another. Even the few years of drought during the 1930's enabled the short-grasses of the dry steppe to invade the territory of the taller grasses. These latter were in turn repatriated when moisture increased.

Actually the belts of natural vegetation do not, in North America, run horizontally east and west across the map like the torrid, temperate, and frigid zones of temperature so neatly figured in the old geographies. A diagonal drawn from northern New England to Southern California passes from a region of high rainfall and low evaporation, along a gradient of lessening rainfall and increasing evaporation, culminating in an arid climate. Had one been able to fly along this diagonal before the European invasion of this continent, he would have passed over forest that gave way to a landscape of scattered trees amid tallgrasses. Then trees would be left behind and gradually the taller grasses would vanish into dry steppe; this in turn would pass into scrub and finally scrub into desert. If such a flight had ended in Baja California it would have revealed a long narrow peninsula lying between the Gulf of California and the Pacific Ocean, almost completely arid despite the encompassing water.

To round out the pattern, our mythical aeronaut should have flown north from Baja to what we now call the Pacific Northwest. This would have brought him back into a region of humid forest climate from which he could then swing eastward, once more crossing interior grasslands, to his takeoff in the forests of Maine or Quebec.

While the irregular forms of the great landmasses and the presence of mountain chains often obscure this pattern, it applies in principle to the vast and complex Eurasian landmass as well as to North America. Even more obscurely, it applies in mirror image to the Southern Hemisphere, where continental land is considerably less. Thus, the eastern margins of both Asia and North America have a forest climate. So do the northwestern areas of Europe and North America. In both great landmasses a gradient headed southwest leads across grasslands (prairie in North America, steppe in Eurasia) to desert (Lower California here, Asia Minor and North Africa in the Old World). Corresponding to the gradient in our West Coast (Lower California to Oregon) there is the line of increasing humidity from North Africa through Iberia into Scandinavia.

South of the equator, where man presumably originated, the pattern of climate and vegetation cannot be so handily diagramed. Yet there, both in the Old and New Worlds, forest savanna, grassland, scrub, and desert are present, although the species and even families of plants may be very different. And beyond the limits of the United States lie tropical forests to the south, treeless tundra and icefields to the north of the Canadian spruce forests.

To generations in western Europe and eastern North America the presence of forests or their remnants has been a normal and familiar aspect of nature. But men elsewhere—and unquestionably our own ancestors at times—have been creatures of open, treeless landscapes. As my own experience of grassland, scrub, and desert has broadened I have been able to work with students of earth, climate, and man as well as fellow biologists. Thanks to them, an interest which began a lifetime ago has grown into a lively appreciation of the part played in human affairs by those vast treeless areas which flourish in continental climates.

The late Senator Lee of Oklahoma used to describe his boyhood home as a place "where one could look farther and see less than anywhere else." Hopefully the following pages may enrich the view, and even extend it.

chapter two

Beyond the Forest

THE great adventure we call life on this planet began some two or more billion years ago when the earth was about half its present age. The experiment—for what else can you call persistent trial and error, elimination and success—that has resulted in man goes back a mere seventy-five million years or so. Flowering plants were replacing more primitive forms, and reptiles were giving way to mammals when the first primates appeared.

These precursors of man and other modern primates made their debut in a world clad largely with trees. For such a world they possessed two invaluable features—good vision for judging distance, and grasping forefeet (ancestral to our thumb and fingers). A great improvement on the claws of cat and squirrel, these hands-to-be foreshadowed a wealth of manipulative experience denied to other forms of life, which ultimately, we believe, served as a stimulus to increasing brain-power.

The fossil record has often been compared to the remains of a vast

15

library from which most volumes are lost and from whose remaining books many pages have been torn. Yet from this scant and broken source we know that biological innovations are followed by countless modifications, most of which do not succeed. As time goes on, the successful modifications of any group of plants or animals boil down to relatively few, although the numbers of individuals of such kinds may become exceedingly great. Man, with his present billions, is a prime example.

Some thirty million years ago, with the primates at mid-age, earth's climates began a slow, profound change. The moist and equable conditions required by forests shrank in extent. Zones of cold and dryness developed, offering niches to the rich variety of low-growing plant life, better suited than trees to these harsher conditions. These were mostly flowering plants, herbaceous and woody, except in colder regions where mosses and lichens held their ground. The most versatile and successful of these replacements of the forest were the grasses. This remarkable group of flowering plants includes species adapted to a wide range of growing conditions and possessed of many virtues. Their growth and vigor do not suffer when their leaf tips are bitten or cut off. The seedlike fruit of grasses is a neat package of usually well balanced nutriment, while the fibrous roots branching through the soil hold the grasses in place against the force of wind and weather.

Thus vast pastures opened up, to be followed by a burst of vegetarian mammals, from great hoofed ungulates to rodents. And in their wake the eaters of flesh, to say nothing of the swarms of insects and microorganisms that rapidly developed to take advantage of new and varied opportunity.

This gradual opening up of the landscape not only afforded new means of subsistence, it also gave a freedom of movement impossible in unbroken forest. Although living organisms had accomplished marvels of diffusion to all the continents, thanks to shifting patterns of land and sea during the preceding multimillions of years, migration during the late Tertiary took on new dimensions. Unforested communities of the open landscape tended to spread until they were checked by conditions that gave trees the advantage; animal life following *en suite* with the vegetation that sustained it.

Into this great innovation the primates, the precursors of both man and his not always acknowledged relatives, were swept. True, many

Lowland scrub in overgrazed grassland, the Grand Tetons.

remain until this day as forest dwellers. But for the more adventurous the transition from green jungle to open parkland was not too abrupt. Forest passes into grassland by degrees, with clumps of trees, separated by herbaceous growth, forming the savanna which borders the forest edge. As birdwatchers and hunters know, these mixtures of trees and intervales exhibit what is known as "edge effect," being richer in small animal life than the unbroken forest. They are also likely to be well supplied with easily harvested fruits, nuts, and other edible plant parts.

That the forerunners of modern man (hominids, we call them) tested various ways of life seems clear from the work of Dr. and Mrs. Louis L. Leakey. These remarkable investigators, whose fifteen years of scratching around in the Olduvai Gorge of southern Africa is proof that science is an act of faith, have found two groups of early hominids. One, with teeth early worn down, they believe to be vegetarian. The other, with undamaged teeth, they regard as meat-eaters. These groups in their judgment lived side by side, much as the hunting pygmies and farming Masai do to this day.

Every branch of science has been enlisted in the effort to reconstruct the epic wanderings of the primates. Physics, for example, has furnished the means to date ancient organic stuff. Astronomy and geology are unraveling the history of the climatic changes so fateful to living beings. Paleontology and archeology continue their task of restoration, striving to bridge the vast gap between fossil remains and the tangible evidences of early human activity.

As a rough working guide we shall not be far off if we assume that man is a phenomenon of the last million years, although recent work tends to push back his origin beyond that point. While a million years is a long time in terms of human experience, it is a mere 1/5000 of earth time, making man a parvenu in planetary history.

The psalmist asked, "What is Man, that Thou are mindful of him?" Science, mindful in its own less poetic way, repeats the question, increasingly convinced that our own species *Homo sapiens* is not the only, nor the first that deserves to be called human. We need not involve ourselves in these technical matters to be confident that human beings have been obliged during the past million years to live in an exceptionally turbulent period of geological history. For this period has been that of the great Pleistocene glaciations. During this time in contrast to the generally more serene and uniform pattern of past climate, there was, and still is, a vast patchwork of climates ranging among extremes of temperature, moisture, and manifold combinations of both.

More than this, these different climates have not remained fixed in area and position throughout human time. Four (we are reasonably certain) massive advances of ice sheets have crowded the zones of climate equatorward, while three great interglacials and a possible fourth in which we live have reversed the process. Roughly speaking, this reversal has expanded the open landscapes of desert and grassland that favor motility of man and other animals.

Paradoxically, the accumulation and advance of glacial ice (itself a barrier and unfavorable to desert and grassland) is fed by the evaporation of sea water and consequent lowering of sea level. This lowering in turn opens up land bridges between continents and islands, across which, as we well know, life, including our own, has been able to move. But this opportunity is at its height when on the land masses themselves open landscape is at a minimum due to the presence of ice. Thus men have had to make their way over the earth by a kind of artful dodging as chance opened up pathways.

In the course of his dispersal, man developed the use of fire and the shaping of tools from stone. In this fashion the gatherer of grubs, fruits, and roots became the hunter. Luckily for him, the open landscapes that favored his movement were also a lavish source of animal protein, while the streams along which prehistoric camp and village sites were concentrated furnished him both water and additional food.

Yet during most of the last million years, progress (if we may use that term) in man's way of life was agonizingly slow. Most of his energy was consumed in the search for food and the struggle to stay alive. His migrations were interrupted by glacial advances such as that which forced the reindeer hunters into southern Europe, obliging them to retreat from more northerly stations which they occupied during times of more genial climate.

The last glaciation, which we call the Wisconsin in North America, the Würm in Europe, reached its greatest extent about eighteen thousand years ago. This was followed by a vacillating retreat which finally cleared northern United States and Germany about ten thousand years ago. Then, as the zones of vegetation and animal life shifted poleward once more, two fateful developments took place. Curiously enough, these represented refinements of the two modes of subsistence which, as Louis

Leakey reports, had characterized two different species of primitive hominids living in Africa some millions of years earlier.

In the great grasslands of Eurasia hunters who followed the herds of grazing animals gradually domesticated the more amenable species, by a process unknown but not difficult to guess. Most likely this came about by capture and rearing of the helpless young—a familiar sight around military camps and still practiced, I have observed, with antelope in Baja California and western Nebraska.

In the still more open landscape of arid lands through which rivers descended from the watered and forested mountains, large-fruited grasses and other plants which had been used as foods came to be cultivated. Again, we have a reasonable guess as to how this came about. Prehistoric dwelling sites have sometimes been located by their concentration of phosphorous compounds from human wastes. These with the accompanying nitrates and ashes from camp fires would have provided fertile growing conditions for the rejected seeds of edible plants. Such spontaneous gardens must have suggested the possibility of cultivation. One may see even today, thickets of tomato plants where cannery waste has been deposited. Not long ago, sitting on the terrace of a country home, I looked down on a tangle of watermelon vines covering the sloping bank beyond, testimony of rejected seeds tossed out on summer afternoons.

Whatever the details, these two great advances and combinations of them made it possible for human beings to have some respite from the unending search for food. Life in more or less organized groups instead of wandering families gave the leisure to develop arts. Among the nomadic followers of herds, physically active and (especially after the taming of the horse) highly mobile and aggressive, raiding and warfare became characteristic.

In contrast, the more sedentary gardeners and farmers faced the problem of controlling water, reckoning time, designing permanent shelters, and organizing institutional life with its attendant systems of thought and belief. New utensils, tools, and weapons were devised; and as pressure of numbers grew it became possible to expand a kind of agriculture into forested land, cleared by axe and fire.

Fundamentally there has been—and still is—incompatibility between nomad and farmer. The former is subject to the hardships of unfavorable years. The latter is vulnerable to raiding. Both often covet the same ground. The symbolism of Cain and Abel is a recurring theme throughout man's experience, erring perhaps chiefly in its suggestion that the herdsman Abel was a gentle soul. (The qualities of cattle are not likely to be absorbed by the man who handles them, although I did know an unlovely character whose remarkable success with swine was attributed by a neighbor to the fact that he shared their point of view.)

The western world has long regarded the earth as existing for man to use and manipulate as he sees fit. Opposed to this is the idea of environmental determinism, holding that man and his cultures are products of environment. But one need not regard the human being as a passive object in the midst of environmental forces in order to appraise their vital role. Natural selection, acting through the ages on the mixture of heritable tendencies which we call the gene complex, has assured that environment has, so to speak, been built into the very fabric of life. It follows, I believe, that airy assumptions of man's complete "control of nature" are specious.

Probably what confuses the issue is the fact that, save for the more or less autonomous bodily functions, man is linked to environment through the forms of his particular culture. And for the most part, we are all more immediately aware of the impact of the culture about us than of the physical compulsions to which that culture has been, historically, an attempt to adjust.

Nowhere is this better shown than in the influence of the open landscape on human society. Cradles of domestication, open landscapes have nurtured great empires based on agriculture. But bordering these developments were steppe and desert whose inhabitants survived by virtue of free movement and aggressiveness. Whether we consider the invasions of Rome and China, Kitchener's campaign in the Sudan, the warlike plains and peaceable pueblo cultures of our Southwest, or even the Populist movement, we are dealing with the interplay of forces having their origin in the economics of environment.

So important to man is the open landscape that as soon as his techniques permitted he addressed himself to enlarging it at the expense of forest. Wood, the reserve stuff of the forest, consists mainly of materials indigestible to us, though useful, while those of grassland can be made to furnish nutrition. Hence our long-standing ambivalence toward woodland, source of fuel and fiber, yet rival for space and obstacle to free movement. In the modern world grasslands have become our granaries and source of animal protein.

Although the Atlantic seaboard was forested, saw and axe permitted its rapid clearance and conversion to agriculture before the opening of the grasslands to settlement. With the foothold of energy and security thus insured, Yankee ingenuity devised the economic innovation of mass production two decades before the Erie Canal furnished an outlet for western agriculture. With its early advantages of wealth and location, the East established and has largely kept a controlling hand in the economy that developed with western settlement.

Since the minerals necessary to modern industry are where we find them, quite independently of climatic patterns, their location modifies earlier and simpler distributions of activity and power. The great metropolises, no longer dependent upon the local food supply that made them possible, now reach their tentacles far out to the sources of raw materials, whose processing yields greater profits than their extraction. Without the water which falls beyond its borders and the food produced at remote distances, no modern city could long survive.

Even the arid desert lands are under pressure. For the warmer of these have the gift of winter sunshine along with fertile soil that lacks only moisture to make it productive. Preempted by the first settlers for irrigation, the often precarious water supply is now called upon to sustain growing populations of those with sufficient means to escape the gloom and rigors of rugged winters in new urban complexes. Many of these are the sad-faced widows left in loneliness by the strain of business, or whatever it is that explains the shorter life span of American males. Many are farmers living either on their accumulated earnings or on money from the sale of rich prairie farms.

To serve these growing numbers of refugees from the cold, thriving enterprises in real estate and services have developed. Thus, in a fashion the flow of wealth into older urban centers has been reversed, but only by increased pressure upon the open landscape. Removal of even the scant desert vegetation produces dust, which along with the effluvia of smelters, refineries, and automotive traffic, impairs the once breathable air. Irrigation, the most extravagant use of water, suffers the threat of displacement by more remunerative use of its space for urban development. Water for domestic consumption has top priority, industrial use generally next, and agriculture last.

Already the older regions of the North American continent are being called upon to finance new sources of water, whether by costly desalting of the seas or by the construction of great reservoirs. In such fashion and in many other ways the ancient patterns of migration, interplay, and pressure take on new forms in response to environmental differences as human numbers increase and cultures become more complex and powerful.

chapter three

The Kinds of Open Space

BORN in the forest, man emerged from it and grew to his present stature largely by using, eventually by enlarging, an open landscape. Today he faces the problem of designing a homestead that will best serve him and his descendants. Unlike his ancestors, he seems to have solved two great challenges—the acquiring of knowledge and the production of things.

One essential art remains to be mastered. The western world has been notably reluctant to listen to and learn from its critics, domestic or foreign. This fault applies not only to those warnings which reach us through the written or spoken word but to the tacit criticisms presented to us by examples of other ways of life. Our besetting flaw is our determination, whether from compassion or desire for profit, to mold other cultures into the likeness of our own.

To mold our own landscape is a far more useful enterprise. Before deciding what we want we must know what we have. The truly great architect is one who tempers his dreams of perfection with respect for the resources and needs of his client. Arts seem to be at their greatest when they are struggling with the limitations of whatever medium they employ. Rodin, in speaking to Malvina Hoffman, mentioned with contempt what he called "accursed facility."

The only hope of estimating the amount of open landscape on earth is by subtraction. Forested land has high visibility. The best educated guess we have is that Canada, the United States, and Europe are 40 percent forested, the rest of the world, 60 percent. Reversing these figures gives us the percentages that are now unforested. But it tells us little about what open space under present conditions has the potential to produce forest.

There are several kinds of open landscape. Their classification is complicated by our still imperfect knowledge, by the great variety of colloquial names, by differences in organisms due to evolutionary history, and by the enormous variation in climatic and other natural controls.

In a very general way, however, each great landmass shows: 1. *Communities dominated by tallgrasses,* in North America called prairies. In South America they are known as pampas, while in Europe they form the western more humid portion of the steppes. 2. *Shortgrass communities,* called the high plains in North America, and occupying most of the steppeland in the Eurasian continent. In Australia they form the desert margin. 3. *Desert.* Considerable portions of desert, notably in southwestern North America, are in reality open forests of giant cacti or tree forms of the lily family, such as *Yucca.* Other areas, such as the chaparral of our West, dry, low-growing woody thickets, are called scrub and often called semidesert. 4. *Tundra,* lying poleward beyond forest limits and above timber line in high mountain regions.

The borders of great plant formations are seldom sharply defined. Rather they are separated by transition zones, forming a continuum. Thus forest grades into prairie by means of outliers interspersed among grassy areas, either as upland groves or the gallery forests along stream valleys. The former are savannas, while the latter are flood-plain and ravine woodlands, for example in Nebraska and Kansas.

Prairie in turn shades into shortgrass as a mixture of tall bunchgrasses, separated from the shorter ones much as prairie groves are separated by natural meadow.

Approach to the desert may be signaled by sparser types of shortgrass or actual grass desert, often called desert grassland. Quite frequently the

Desert shrubs and grasses, Baja California.

transition consists of woody scrub. One encounters this in driving through northern Mexico, south from Laredo, Texas, in much of Arizona and New Mexico, and farther north in the sagebrush region of the Great Basin.

Tundra, whether on high mountain tops or in the arctics, replaces dense conifer forest as the latter frays out into open stands of stunted and deformed trees. Grasses and their near-relatives the sedges are present, but are largely replaced by sodden mosses, lichens in drier spots, and tiny birches and willows.

Probably because trees seemed to the explorers and settlers from western Europe the normal and natural kind of plant life, their extensive absence has evoked a surprising variety of explanations. No fewer than ten—each with its vigorous advocates—were listed in the scientific literature at the turn of the century. These included fire, grazing by bison herds, irregular rainfall, and less plausibly fine soil texture as causes. Aridity was implied by early references to the grassland province as the "Great American Desert." Explanations were further complicated by the great variation in temperature and length of growing season from the Gulf coast to northern Canada.

Actually, fire, whether set by lightning or man, has been a frequent and spectacular event, especially in the tallgrass prairie. Its disastrous effect on trees is clear enough. After settlement, when fire in such border states as Illinois became less frequent thanks to mowing and plowing, woodland began to appear on the western, prairieward stream borders. This promptly led to the belief that the same thing would happen farther on into the grassland itself—an assumption whose test was hampered by the rapid conversion from sod to agriculture.

Even today some highly respectable scientists lean to the opinion that fires set by "early man" (a relative term on the different continents) have been responsible for converting primeval forests into grassland. This idea has been urged despite the evidence that, however enthusiastic a pyromaniac man may be, lightning is a far more consistent and effective igniter. When a distinguished scientist defended the arson theory and decried the notion that lightning could have played a part, a friend, a former student of the speaker, slyly reminded me of the time we had both helped put out a small prairie fire in Oklahoma, set by the thunder-bolts of Jove.

The truth is that two of the alleged causes of grassland—fire and grazing—have always been a part of its normal regime. Just as forest

Two views of virgin prairie, small flowers, yucca and grasses.

rebounds from fire and hurricane, trees replacing trees, so it is with grassland, except where it borders on forest. There, fire decides the precarious balance between the two competing types of vegetation in favor of grass.

But in prairie, as the late Professor Curtis of Wisconsin showed quite clearly, occasional fire is not only endured but serves a useful function. In the prolonged absence of fire dead dry stubble containing stems, leaves, and other rubbish accumulates. Growth and vigor of the grasses and other plants suffer visibly, whatever the mechanism—be it basal shading, locking up of mineral nutrients, or a combination of factors. Under these conditions fire acts as a release, followed by reestablishment of the prairie.

Grazing too helps remove excessive growth and through its contribution of animal wastes, returns nutrient minerals to the soil. With occasional fires, it helps maintain the remarkable stability of grassland. This of course is not true where either of these conditions becomes too intense and persistent.

As to soil, it is true that over vast expanses of the grasslands of North America and doubtless in other continents the texture is fine. The newcomer who looks for a stone to shy at a rabbit or unfriendly dog is in for disappointment, as I know from experience. This characteristic of the soil so impressed the Swiss Leo Lesquereux, a good naturalist of the late nineteenth century, that he suggested that grassland was due to the absence of coarse soil materials. (He had not reckoned with the fact that as one moves westward across the Mississippi valley toward the mountains, sands and gravels and finally larger stones do make their appearance in grassland soils.)

Through the ages wind and water have carved away at mountains as they arose, wore down, and arose again. The mountain torrents which in spring tumble great rocks about as a small boy might rattle the marbles in his pocket drop the heaviest stones first, and carry the lightest particles farthest out. Winds, too, which in the desert can often be seen to roll pebbles along, lift up the finer stuff and carry it long distances. In the past, at times when rock flour was particularly abundant and plant cover meager, wind-blown material was dropped to form thick deposits often far from its source.

This fine material forms vertical cliffs such as those that are plainly visible along the Mississippi near Vicksburg. But fine-textured soil is not a primary cause of treeless regions. Trees will thrive on it if other conditions are right. The question then is, what are the conditions which so largely discourage forests over much of the earth?

The answer, long delayed by our lack of knowledge, lies primarily in climate. The best of our records are surprisingly recent. They began with crude measuring devices during the early nineteenth century in Europe. In our own West many records were started at frontier military outposts. At first only the more obvious and easily measured factors received attention—temperature, rainfall, wind direction and velocity.

With such limited data at hand, it was difficult to invoke climate to explain the presence of prairie at Lincoln, Nebraska, with its twenty-seven-inch rainfall as against Columbus, Ohio, with only thirty-four per year. Farther west, in shortgrass and desert no instruments were needed to determine greater dryness. If common sense failed, the famous jackass pluviometer, whose rope tail is wet when it rains and dry otherwise, would have done.

But for regions of substantially equal rainfall the evaporating power of the air must be taken into account. This factor is still difficult to measure, and has been long neglected for that reason. Not long after the first spotty and rough data on evaporation became available students of vegetation began to realize that the drying power of the air must be considered in reckoning the net amount of water available to support plant life.

Using the very meager data available, Dr. Edgar N. Transeau of Ohio State University came up with the suggestion that only where the amount of rainfall in inches per year exceeded the drying capacity of the air, measured in the same units, were natural forests likely to become established. Where the ratio of rainfall to evaporation was less than one to one, grassland, scrub, or desert, progressively as the ratio grew less, were to be found.

Although land forms, temperatures, and soil materials vary greatly from place to place, the general principle seems sound enough. The much more extensive and precise measurements now possible tend to reinforce it. Among the interesting exceptions to the effect of dry climate is the extension of woods into grassland climate where loose sandy soils occur, as in the Cross-Timbers of Oklahoma and Texas that Washington Irving once described. The explanation appears to be that rainfall soaks into such soils faster than it does into finer soils around these woodlands. Thus a greater proportion of rainfall gets underground where it is protected from the drying power of sun and wind. Even more important is the fact that during critical periods of dryness sandy soils will yield their water to plant roots more readily than the tighter clays and silts.

Mutatis mutandis, tongues of tallgrasses characteristic of subhumid climate extend into regions of shorter and sparser vegetation of semi-arid climate where there is sandy soil and, other things being equal, shortgrass behaves in like fashion at the desert margin. In short, the great open areas of natural vegetation are determined by climate, with available moisture serving as the chief limiting factor, often subject to local influences such as soil texture.

So well established is this principle that climatologists, a tough-minded breed, now speak routinely of subhumid, semiarid, and arid landscapes, meaning respectively the tallgrass prairie, shortgrass plains or steppes, and desert. In fact, these designations are coming to be used interchangeably, although the crucial test of any classification of climates is the character of the living communities which would develop in the absence of human interference.

This is one of the several excellent reasons why generous samples or specimens of natural vegetation should be preserved. No one would think of destroying the standards upon which our units of measurement are based, or the tables of constants used to assure the exactness of physics and chemistry. Industry would roar like a wounded lion at such a threat to the technology which assures its profits. Yet the destruction of the standards essential to an understanding of climate (and biological process) has gone on since the settlement of North America with no justification stronger than immediate profit. The only exception has been the setting aside of public reserves for sustained yield and recreation, to a lesser extent for aesthetic reasons, by both public and private agencies. Only recently has their scientific importance been emphasized to support the longer view, both economic and aesthetic.

Not all naturally open landscape is a direct response to the general climate in which it is found. Tundra differs from grassland and desert in flourishing where water is abundant. This, however, is an illusory advantage. Save for shallow surface melting during the brief growing season, the water is locked up by cold. It is of no good to plant life in the form of ice; and it is certainly insufficient, as is the short growing season, to support trees. There are other complications as well. Low temperatures slow down the cycling of mineral nutrients by decay, lessening the meager fertility of cold soils. Under these conditions the soil system, such as it is, becomes acid, another circumstance hostile to luxuriant vegetation.

Among the many intriguing aspects of vegetation is the fact that substantial specimens of both grassland and tundra communities are found where, in terms of climate, they seem not to belong. Both occur as enclaves, for example, in the otherwise originally forested states of the North Central group, adjacent to the Great Lakes. Plants and even animal life here are in many respects similar to, often identical with, those of the great climatic zones which they resemble. Until these homes away from home were virtually obliterated, the grasses, goldenrods, rattlesnakes, and many insects of the Ohio prairie outliers were those of the Illinois and Iowa prairies. The same thing was true, to a lesser extent, of the bogs once found in the Buckeye state, with their populations of northern species.

For a comparison not too inapt, we may cite the French Quarter in New Orleans, Chinatown in San Francisco, and even the beer gardens in St. Louis and Milwaukee where remnants of early settlement have persisted. As the life which had been driven southwestward by the ponderous advance of the glaciers moved back slowly in the wake of the final retreat pioneer communities were overtaken in turn by those from warmer reservoirs. But here and there groups of northern plants survived, particularly in the cool and sheltered basins of dying lakes, remaining as sphagnum bogs.

Still later, the warming and drying that had driven back the great continental ice masses along their northeast-southwest gradient reached a climax of warmth and dryness some three to four thousand years ago. Curiously enough the stubborn bog societies held on in spite of this hostile atmosphere. But the evergreen, and other forests on the uplands around them, gave way to more warmth-loving kinds. We have ample reason to believe that the warm, dry climate at this time gave grassland an advantage over forest and that the prairie province advanced well to the east of its present limits.

About the beginning of the Christian era, the turning point in modern calendars, there occurred a turning point in climate. Slowly it became cooler and more humid, giving forests once more the advantage. More precisely, the humid area expanded and the great concentric zones of plant and animal life, ranged in order of their water requirements, moved southwestward to reoccupy land that had been for millennia too dry for

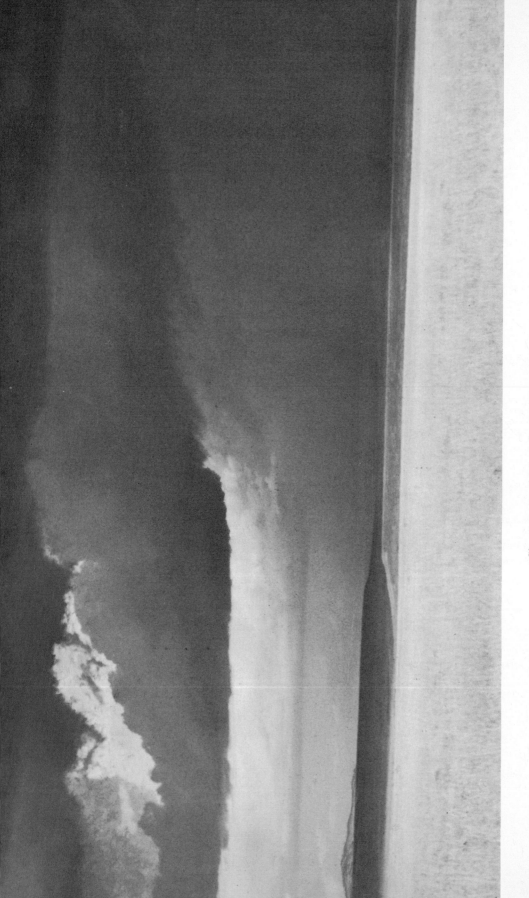

Shortgrass on high plains, New Mexico.

them. As they did so, pockets of the displaced communities were passed by, to become such enclaves as the grassland remnants in the North Central states. Just what enabled these relics to hang on is not clear, for some were on poorly drained sites, others on sites so well drained as to be too dry to encourage the growth of trees.

Persistence of living communities in *refugia* despite unfavorable surroundings has its parallels in human history. The protection may be cultural—a way of life—as it has been for three hundred years with the Pennsylvania Dutch. Or protection may be environmental, as forest serves the African pygmies on the fringes of a grazing economy or forest and bog aided the Celts in their defiance of the Romans along the Scottish border. The same Lesquereux who thought the prairies were a result of soil texture, wondered why willows and other trees of their kind did not invade wet meadows and grassed swamps more readily, and observed that they did so where rare presence of a soggy fallen log gave them a foothold. Nor is there much reason to doubt that Indian fires, keeping back the forest at its advancing front, helped the rear guards of the retreating grasslands to maintain their hold.

Not all of the open landscapes within the forest domain are survivors from more arid times, or from colder ones. Lava flows, marching dunes, tidal estuaries, and freshwater marshes, beaver meadows (where forest has been drowned by these industrious engineers), and bare surfaces of granite such as Stone Mountain in Georgia are all examples of the effect of local conditions that override the generosity of climate. Many of these systems are transient, for living systems tend to move toward more or less complete expression of the general environment. But this development is so slow in some as to be imperceptible on our scale of measurement, for example on the barren surface of the indurated lavas in Mexico and Hawaii.

But of all the forces that tend to create and maintain an open treeless landscape, man is today the most potent. It makes little difference whether one is inclined to make a distinction between natural and human phenomena, or to side with the dictum of George Perkins Marsh that man had become (as he wrote in 1863) a major natural force both geological and biological. By 1825 New England, once solidly forested except for its wetlands and a few minor areas, had become at least 75 percent cleared. A century later the forest area of Ohio had shrunk from 90 to 15 percent.

Eastern China and much of India, both with forest climate, have long since been denuded of their original forest cover—a costly change which the present governments are trying desperately to reverse. Place names reveal that the Balkans once had great forests, some places dominated by beech, others by oak.

It is an axiom of biology that the strongest potential competitor of a species is its own kind, man being no exception. But it is also true that civilization, whether nurtured in dry or humid centers, has almost invariably grown both by virtue of and at the expense of forest. Man has a double motive for his removal of forest. He needs its wood for construction and fuel. And he desires the space it occupies to provide room for his fields and his structures and range for his domestic animals.

With monotonous regularity in western China, the Near East, and the Americas, as manpower and tools made it possible, deforestation has rippled outward from the centers of power. Almost without exception it has expanded into the wooded uplands. These green-clad hills, in their original state, not only furnished abundant water but regulated its movement and safeguarded the fertile lowlands against both shortage and the disaster of flood.

During Carolingian times there was massive destruction of forests in western Europe. Doubtless many factors were responsible. One was probably the need for new tillage space. Another may have been facilitation of military operations, like the defoliation and burning of forest lands in Viet Nam. Dense woodlands favor guerrilla operations over more conventional warfare. Clearly, a third factor was charcoal manufacture. This forest product was not only invaluable for small controlled domestic cooking fires, but until the use of coke in modern times charcoal was the source of carbon as an alloy of iron in the making of steel. Deforestation reached a peak in the days of Charlemagne when weaponry was a major industry.

To these uses we must of course add structural needs. In short, as civilization spread during the period A.D. 400–800, it did so at the expense of the original forest cover. The chief exceptions thereafter were the hunting preserves set apart by monarchs and nobles, and the gradual establishment of municipal and other community woodlands.

Among the better known great hunting preserves are the New Forest in southern England and those of the Imperial Court of Russia. Community forests are still a feature of the Swiss landscape. The famous Wiener Wald of Vienna, whose citizens refused to cut it for fuel during the occupation of World War II, is a somewhat special case, since the

Swiss forests are maintained for harvest of timber and the Vienna Woods for amenity.

There are woods that have been preserved for religious and ceremonial reasons. To the followers of Buddha and Baal, as to the Druids, trees have been sacred and groves places of worship. When the children of Israel strayed from the worship of Jehovah they placed idols among the trees in the fashion of their Canaanite neighbors. Returning to the faith, their kings and prophets smashed the idols and cut down the "groves" according to the King James Version of the Bible. Happily, modern scholars have discovered that this did not mean the clearing away of living trees but of the wooden images of Asherah, a mother goddess whose name has been translated into English as "groves."

Though the Near East has suffered from the destruction of its mountain forests, the royal poet David could liken the righteous to trees growing by living water. His son Solomon was obliged to import timber for the temple from the realm of his friend Hiram, king of Tyre.

In short, among the many contradictions in man's nature is his curious ambivalence toward two primeval benefactors—trees and grass. In his wanderings over the earth, which had taken him into every habitable continent before the dawn of history, he was sustained by the generosity of forest and steppe. Yet unfailingly, as his need required and his technical power enabled him to do so, he assaulted both with fire, axe, plow, goats, and other grazing animals.

Woodlands—source of fruits, game, fuel, and shelter—have also hidden his enemies. After the invention of agriculture and man's spread from the irrigated treeless centers of civilization trees became his rivals for space. Even today with the unplanned spread of urban life axe and bulldozer precede the builder of home and industry, destroying islands of natural beauty and amenity. The incoming homeowner becomes charged to restore shade, greenery, and even productive soil with painful slowness as best he can.

The open landscapes which man first encountered were an expression of climate or more local conditions of soil and drainage. Those of today are increasingly the result of his own activities, thus cultural in their origin. How far he can go in creating places for living which unlike those he found do not make efficient use of energy and materials in biological processes, may ultimately determine his survival.

chapter four

And the Earth Brought Forth Grass

WHETHER greensward—green either by art or nature—was ever considered sacred, I do not know. There may be more unconscious ritual with us than we realize. After one builds his house on a plot of ground, whether in usually moist New England or the desert air of Salt Lake City, his first concern is to create a grassy lawn. Trees are an afterthought.

There are sound evolutionary reasons why green falls upon a grateful eye. You may call them biochemical if you will, for they are. Yet there may be more than this, lost in a forgotten past when green gave the promise of food and water for man and beast. Today our lawns are carpets. Sanctuaries are properly floored with rich carpeting. The golfer, stealing his hour from the speed and harassment of modern affairs, is moved by the beauty, no less than the challenge, of a perfect green. Man may reason with his marvelous forebrain, but he still has behind it the cerebellum that guides him from below the threshold of his awareness.

These reflections are not all proved and therefore not scientific in the current fashion. The range of instinct so far as man is concerned is still moot. A prevailing school regards man as almost completely plastic, product of training and learning. The recent suggestion, tracing him back to the carnivorous *Australopithecus africanus,* that he may be an instinctive killer has at least the merit of stirring up inquiry. Wherever the truth may lie, our evolutionary animal nature cannot be ignored, however we may build upon it for good or ill. The wary crow and shy whooping crane that remain behind with a wounded comrade as I have seen crows do, give us reason to believe that not all ethical behavior is a wholly recent novelty invented by a reluctant primate.

Certainly we have reason enough to know that many viewing the great natural grasslands with their incessant play of movement and color have been stirred to depths that go beyond any shallow aesthetic appreciation.

As to the regard given individual species of the grass family we need not be so cautious. Three great grasses, not to mention others, have served to free man from the incessant quest for food, making possible cities and the leisure arts. Each has had its place in the religion of its beneficiaries. Whether or not the plants themselves were worshipped, wheat, rice, and maize has each had its appropriate divinity. The Greek Demeter, goddess of grain and harvest, became the Ceres of the practical Romans. The Orient had its rice goddess and the Aztecs the sponsoring divinities for maize.

Each of these indispensable cereals had its ritual at the times of planting and harvest, emperors and kings no less than priests and common people taking part in the ceremonies. "The corn goddesses," George Vaillant says of the Aztecs, "were young and lovely . . . the embodiments of young growth and, by analogy, youth and the games." Their male counterparts had similar significance. Within recent years I have seen, in remote parts of Central America, small pillars of rough stone in the center of newly planted fields, probably to reenforce or perhaps to hedge the promise of churchly prayer.

Dance, legend, and the mystic ceremonies of the kiva among our Southwestern Indians preserved and expressed the gratitude of simple folk for what must have been from their point of view nothing less than a miraculous gift of gods to man. Even the pollen of the maize played its part as a sacred golden dust.

From what we know of earlier times in human history, gratefulness and concern were not the only virtues thus manifest. There was no lack of intelligence among those who have preceded us during the millennia. True, they had not hit upon the approach to the ways of nature that we call science. Yet they had learned much from trial and error, costly as such information is. Among other things, they understood that fertility and production are complex phenomena, depending upon a number of conditions.

Thousands of years before the great German chemist Baron von Liebig announced his Law of the Minimum, which states that production was governed by the least favorable factor, folk-wisdom knew that a chain is no stronger than its weakest link. In the idiom then understood, soil, water, air, light, and plant life itself were each associated with appropriate divinities. Success involved rituals of placation and worship, but it also invested good husbandry with the sanction of belief. Even now one can find neighbors who staunchly hold to the rule that root crops must be planted in the dark of the moon, seed crops in its light. Right or wrong, old folkways have remarkable vitality.

The ancients could not, of course, put a finger on each of the nutrient elements of the soil, nor did they by any means know all that is needed for optimum yields. Yet they knew that much had to be right if the whole system were to be at its best.

If one reads for the first time the classic counsels to husbandmen, beginning with the Greek Hesiod of the eighth century B.C. and running on to Augustan Virgil, he will be struck by the ease with which much of this ancient lore can be translated into the terms of modern science. For marl, read calcium; for wood ashes, read potash; for bones, read phosphorus; for manure, read organic material; and for the advice to rotate with legumes ("the vetch with its rustling pods"), read nitrogen fixation and you have it.

We must recall, too, that the early farmstead and its successor through centuries was a community within itself. No mere mechanism, turned on and off by man, it was a biological system composed of various kinds of plants and animals, largely self-sustaining under human guidance, using and recycling materials in place. In many respects it had the balanced structure of communities in nature, an interwoven fabric of organisms each with its peculiar role in the incessant building up, use, and decomposition for reuse of organic materials.

Such systems, while carrying on at a low key by modern standards, have enormous resilience as forty centuries of Chinese agriculture show so well. The basic economy of the Tigris-Euphrates region also endured far longer than the time that has elapsed since its irrigation was wrecked by Mongol invaders in the thirteenth century. As we place our own land under ever increasing pressure through the use of fossil fuel and modern devices, moving its products to the ends of the earth, discarding much of our waste and bringing in nutrients from far away, we should surely consider the possibility that novelty is not a sure guarantee of prudence.

We are likely to forget that we owe what advantages we possess to domestication. It was this great art that led our race from the life of primitive animal toward civilization. We may reasonably suppose from the variety of weapon types that have been found at the sites of pre-historic kills that different groups once banded together to hunt the last of the mammoths and other large animals that managed to survive the glacial age. Whether this degree of social behavior preceded or followed the growing of crops is a tantalizing problem. Very probably an answer, if diligently sought, lies in the sediments beneath and around Mexico City. Here many skeletons of mammoth, some with dart point of stone embedded in the bone, have been uncovered, having been preserved for some eight thousand years in the sediments of ancient lakes that became swamps and are now dry land.

Unlike the mastodon (giant elephant that browsed on the twigs of spruce and other northern trees), the mammoth was a grazer. This habit of eating grass enabled him to range far south. Here he encountered Stone Age man. Granted that his carcass yielded plenty of meat, his presence near cultivated fields, if they existed at the time, would have been a source of trouble. This we know from the pictures of wild elephants disporting themselves in cane fields in modern times, and can infer from the damage caused by deer in the gardens of Vermont today.

The advent of cultivation on the various continents is clearly shown by the presence in lake sediment of fossil cereal pollen and that of members of the pigweed family (still cultivated for greens and seeds in Mexico). Thus a study of sediments containing mammoth remains should show clearly whether that animal survived until after the beginnings of cultivation. If so, there would have been a double motive for the slaughter which led to his extinction in the Americas. Until recently it was assumed that he had been victim of the climatic change accompanying the waning of the great continental ice sheets, aided perhaps by man-made fires.

As we know from the fate of the bison, the dodo, and the giant birds of New Zealand and Madagascar, the largest game animals are most vulnerable to the hunter, unless they can be tamed. In this event, as with the reindeer, ox, goat, and sheep of the Old World, we have their domesticated and often highly modified descendants still with us. Rumors persist that some Indian tribes succeeded in converting the bison into a domestic animal. If so, they did better than the white man has done, since he quickly found it much easier to work with the descendants of beasts already tamed.

It is difficult if not impossible to conceive of domestication, either of plants or animals, in the absence of grasses. The taming of the several types of cattle—cows, sheep, and goats—that could be sustained on the great continental grasslands of the interior led to the pastoral life. Instead of the scattered families of gatherers and hunters, it became possible for larger bands, clan groups and slaves, to follow the seasons with their wandering herds. Like hunting and gathering this way of life required ample space, but in a different way.

The hunter needed several square miles for each individual so that territory could support only small and scattered groups. This stimulated the migration which spread man to all the great continents at an early time.

In contrast, the taming of large-seeded grasses made possible intensive cultivation and great economy of space, leading to the formation of villages and ultimately of cities. This was classically true of the great staple cereals, rice in the wetlands of southeastern Asia, wheat and maize in the drier but irrigable regions of the Near East and Middle America respectively. Other cereals such as barley, millet, rye, and oats came under cultivation too as climate and soil permitted.

In each instance a complex of other plants, useful for food or fiber, came to be cultivated along with the staple cereals. These included root crops such as taro in the warm Orient; turnip in Europe; lentils, garlic, onions, and flax in the Mediterranean environs; peppers, squash, and beans in the New World. Supplemented where possible by animal protein from fish, fowl, and cattle, these complexes seem to have resulted in a fairly well balanced diet.

Sand-binding grass, important in stabilizing soils, Myrtle Beach, South Carolina.

As populations increased, however, the proportion of food from animal sources became scarcer. Human beings were obliged to depend more largely upon primary sources—the green plants themselves—for nourishment. In one sense this was an economy, for at every step in the food chain from plants, to vegetarian animals, to carnivores, there is a loss that may reach 90 percent of the original production. In another respect it was a danger, increasing the proportion of starches and sugars, only partially offset by such vegetable proteins as those from legumes.

The sedentary nature of cereal cultivation not only made possible the establishment of larger communities but as we have noted, gave leisure to develop organization and arts. The release of even a small minority from food production has been significant. This figure has ranged from perhaps 5 percent in early times to about 20 percent in nineteenth-century United States where it has risen, thanks to improved technology, to over 85 percent.

Early agriculture, so often dependent upon irrigation, stimulated the invention of methods for the control of water and the measurement of land. It also led to improvements in the reckoning of time. Thus mathematics, "Queen and Servant of the Sciences," had its simple beginnings long before the Orient gave us our convenient symbols for reckoning.

By the fifth millennium B.C. agricultural villages had developed into urban centers of power. These early cities seem to have been originally religious and ceremonial centers, seats of priestly influence supposedly necessary to insure good crops and other benefits. Even the primitive hunters (as we infer from the cave paintings of France and Spain and know from our contact with the American Indian) regarded magic as a necessary adjunct to their enterprise.

Inevitably religious centers became political establishments, absorbing personnel not needed to provide food and other necessities. As population grew, so did pressure for food, the need for territorial expansion, and what we call today the problem of unemployment. Thus arose what Lewis Mumford calls "human machinery," men mobilized for great public works such as aqueducts, pyramids, temples, and enforced military service. The armies thus created often served conveniently to invade and conquer additional productive lands.

Meanwhile the domestication of the horse transformed a source of food into a means of quick transportation. The herdsmen of the grassy steppes and semidesert became fast moving, resourceful, and aggressive warriors. The expanding centers of urban power were looked upon with envy, not only because of their riches but as serious rivals for space. Even with infanticide and other more or less ruthless measures of population control the nomadic groups grew in numbers.

This problem has always been compounded by the pulsating character of subhumid and arid climates, where dry years tend to come in groups alternating with successions, variable in length, of years more favorable to the growth of pasture. There have been many attempts to find some predictable mathematical regularity in these fluctuations. Thus far it appears that what one comes up with in the way of so-called cycles depends upon the mathematical assumptions used in working over the raw data, of which we still have too little. Official weather records go back a few score years, while information from the growth rings of trees, now extending back through the Christian era in our own Southwest, enables us to be certain that droughts will recur but not to predict them more exactly.

Even in the brief history of the United States recurrent groups of good years have encouraged development, only to be followed by failure and distress when, inevitably, long drought intervenes. To the nomads of the Old World favorable years brought green and tender grass, making possible the survival and expansion of grazing herds and the well-being of their masters. On the open landscape where free movement is insured it was possible to secure a continuous supply of fresh pasturage by following the seasons.

Aside from the dangers of conflict with rival groups of herdsmen and the pressures of increasing populations of men and cattle the great inevitable hazard of nomadic life was drought. When dry years come, streams and waterholes dry up and plant life is hard pressed to supply sufficient forage. This is notably true where grazing has been heaviest, along well-used routes and near centers where the abundance of previous good years has encouraged an increase in size of herds. Thus faced with disaster and mobile by custom nomads have only mass migration as a choice against starvation. Then, whether as peaceful seekers of help like the brethren of Joseph in Egypt, or as aggressive invaders, they must move toward more favored peripheries.

The record is too imperfect to confirm the idea that the pulsations that brought about periods of desiccation have always been responsible for the incursions of nomads into prosperous and settled communities.

But we can be sure that such invasions have been repeated throughout the centuries. Whether such adventures were triggered by drought or numbers, the latter were surely necessary if mere raiding were to become pillage and conquest.

For these great outward raids, nomadic herdsmen had ample practice within their own grassland and desert territory. The stealing of cattle and camels from adjacent groups has been—and in places still is—a standard custom. Enslavement of human captives accompanied these livestock raids. There could be little chance of survival except in bands. As the size of bands increased and the need for grazing areas grew, conflict with neighbors became a way of life. Grass, not gold, was the coveted object of struggle and the livestock it supported was the visible symbol of wealth. *Pecus,* or "herd," is the root of our word "pecuniary."

On one of the more prosperous Indian reservations I have seen a pasture fronting on the highway stocked with unused ponies. They serve the same function as our own ostentatious display of jewels, furs, and other symbols of wealth. Like hunting, riding, and sailing, which no longer are necessary to ordinary economic life, this manifestation has survived a utility that goes back beyond the days of Abraham.

On the Eurasian landmass two ancient regions of civilization were separated by a distance equal to almost one sixth of the earth's circumference as it measures halfway between equator and North Pole. China, with the longest and in many ways most stable culture in history, occupied most of Asia north of the Himalayas. Rome at her greatest came to occupy a similar expanse in Europe and the Near East. Between these two great centers of power lay the vastness of semiarid and desert land occupied by fierce and aggressive nomadic tribes, with an economy grimly determined by an environment too austere to support conventional agriculture.

Adjacent to these untamed people both to east and west, were the most vulnerable margins of civilized empire. Easily accessible to raid and invasion, they were far from the centers of political and military power needed for their protection. Largely devoted to food production, they were a natural prey for energetic and fast-moving hordes whose narrow margin of subsistence was periodically threatened by the inevitable recurrence of prolonged drought.

Repeatedly the western communities of China were invaded, sacked, and conquered. Repeatedly the invaders were absorbed and the economy restored to working condition, a fresh target for raids by the very kins-men of the previous invaders. The almost rhythmic cycle of marginal conquest, stability, and new conquest thus established was only varied by greater mass invasions that seized the central government, notably the conquest by Genghis Khan in A.D. 1215 and the Manchu in the seven-teenth century.

As suggested by the erection of the Great Wall and the placement of the soldier beneath the scholar and farmer in esteem, China's concern with military matters seems to have been chiefly defensive. Rome, on the other hand, was a military as well as a political enterprise. This probably explains her interest in engineering and medicine, to the virtual exclusion of other fields of applied science. Protection of her wide-flung borders was more active than passive, but as these continued to expand, so did the problem of logistics. Despite her vigor and high organization, aggres-sive defense of Rome's imperial borders became an increasing burden. In this task she not only had to reckon with the forest dwellers of the north, but with the wandering tribes of the Asiatic steppelands, as well.

The Huns, a powerful group of nomads, moved westward from their Asiatic home some time after A.D. 300, developing a technique for living off the productive lands they invaded. Eventually their raids took on the character of mass invasion, great mixed hordes moving across northern Italy and adjacent Gaul, men, women, children, and beasts forming a plundering nation on the move. Other Huns had previously conquered the north of China whence they were driven in the sixth century A.D. as their kinsmen had been expelled from Roman territory little more than a century earlier.

As human beings emerged from the primitive life of hunters and gatherers, two great streams of mankind developed by virtue of inven-tions that responded to environment. Both the domestication of plants and the grazing of animals, strictly speaking, were made possible by open landscapes. The cultivation of wheat and maize came about where arid lands served as the pathway for waters, or centers for their accumulation, as in the Near East and Mexico. The cultivation of rice, a swamp plant, may be presumed to have arisen where these treeless intervals were present in a place of abundant rainfall.

The open grasslands and bordering deserts fostered the taming of grazing herds, giving rise to a rival way of life, as we have seen. In the course of time these separate streams each led to a distinctive culture with its own characteristics of power. From raid and retaliation there arose in time more massive conflict. Registered in the pages of history are the great invasions and conquests by the steppe-folk of Asia and the desperate efforts of sedentary farming civilizations to counter them.

chapter five

Life in the Grasslands

A professional botanist, trained in the European tradition to know the plant kingdom thoroughly, could locate himself fairly well if suddenly transported to a strange place. But even an amateur should be able to tell what climate he is in if surrounded by unfamiliar plant life.

In the great complex of climates and soils of our planet there are many places, however remote from one another, where environmental conditions are quite similar. These are the so-called bioclimatic analogues, so useful in predicting the probable success of introducing forms of life from elsewhere. The plants and animals in such widely separated communities have long since evolved independently, diverging from any common ancestry in the distant past and becoming as different as camel and kangaroo or cactus and Christ's Thorn. (These ancestral relationships are among the most intriguing aspects of life science. The kangaroo for example is more closely related to our opossum than it is to our domestic cattle, while the bison and camel are nearer kin to each other than they are to the kangaroo.)

Thus it is that to the knowing traveler, the old wheeze about Adam and Eve naming the dog because it looked like a dog applies.

Wherever similar environments occur, no matter how far apart they may be, or how different the species of plants and animals, the general aspect tends to be remarkably similar. A desert on any continent looks like a desert, no matter what specific plants (if any) are growing there. The same applies to grasslands, whether semiarid or subhumid, and of course to forest.

There are profound evolutionary and physiological reasons for this. Land plants are anchored in place by their root systems and must accommodate themselves to the ambient conditions of their environment or perish. Structures and functions that made survival a possibility were the passports that qualified their venturesome ancestors to spread to any place they could reach and which would support them.

Invasion and establishment by no means ended the process of trial and error. Continuously the process of variation kept going, held in check by the severe realities of the environment. General features that spelled fitness were retained with many subtle changes of detail which did not violate, but indeed often perfected them. This was true especially of what in plants are called the vegetative features that carry on the routine business of food manufacture, storage, use, and growth. Stems and leaves must do their work in open air with all the hazards thus involved. This is reflected in form, just as the compulsions of climate are revealed in the clothing and shelter that have enabled man to operate in particular climates.

If there are such striking similarities between the plant life of say Asiatic and American steppes or deserts, by what warrant do we say the plants in each continent are not of the same kinds? Chiefly because the identity of a plant rests far less upon the form of its stem and foliage than upon that of its reproductive organs. True, flower and fruit must have their own harmony with environment, but they are not subject to the lifelong impact of external conditions that must be endured by the rest of the plant which bears them. In striking fashion they retain the imprint of their ancestral forms and, in spite of an infinite variety of detail, the structure of their reproductive systems is the technical basis upon which they are classified.

Grass as a pioneer. Broom sedge on an abandoned field where pines are beginning to invade, North Carolina.

Following the statement of a reasonable theory of evolution by Darwin in 1859, the classification of plants and animals has served for more than a set of pigeonholes into which groups, major and minor, can be dropped, necessary as this is. It now is a key to degrees of kinship. Since most of evolution long antedates the human race, this tracing of common ancestries and subsequent changes must involve a considerable degree of imagination and judgment on the part of biologists. The perfection of optical and chemical methods as they reveal the minute structure and composition of organisms has given increasingly precise and critical means of determining relationships. So, too, do breeding experiments. Yet for all this, classification has a large element of art as well as science.

One interesting result of the evolutionary viewpoint has been to show that the groups now having the greatest number and variety of forms (species) are those which are relatively young. On the other hand, those more ancient and primitive, if still surviving, are represented by relatively few kinds. Thus the redwoods, or sequoias, whose fossils are found widely in deposits some hundreds of millions years old, have today only three species alive, two in North America, one in China.

The same situation applies to the horse. Its ancestry is well documented. Fossil remains of numerous species have been found in North America where they originated some 45,000,000 years ago, migrated to the Old World, and disappeared in the New until reintroduced from Europe. Today three species, horse, ass, and zebra remain. A fourth, the quagga, became extinct during the 1870's, a lethal decade for many forms of wild life.

The peculiar qualities of horse, cattle, sheep, and antelope have been developed in intimate relation to open landscape—specifically the grasslands. This is reflected in many ways—teeth, digestive system, herd habit, and notably in the case of horse and antelope, a capacity for swift movement. To some degree the horns of cattle compensate for their relative lack of speed, but the speed of wild and primitive types—even the Texas longhorn—is not to be judged by the placid domestic animals of our range and pastures. Among sheep, the rams are horned while the elusive character of wild sheep and their relatives, goats and chamois, is proverbial.

The sharp, broad incisors of grass-eating animals are beautifully adapted for clipping grass and other herbs, aided in horse and camel by prehensile lips, in cattle by the broad purse-like form of those organs.

Where the more flexible lips more or less wrap around the tufts of forage, the wide, firm ones of the cow sweep them in to be bitten off.

The lips of sheep and goat are thin and close to the biting teeth. For this reason they can and do crop much closer to the base of forage plants. This, plus an apparent incompatibility of odor, helps explain the proverbial dislike of the cattleman for the sheepherder, since sheep not only damage the range but make it unwelcome to the larger animals.

The herbivores, depending as they do so largely upon grass for forage, require special digestive apparatus as compared to those vegetarians whose diet consists of seeds and fruits although the herbivores can, as we know, consume these also. To make the most efficient use of the cell wall stuff of grasses the horse relies upon the peculiar chemistry of its digestive juices. In more deliberate fashion the ruminants—cattle, sheep, camel, goat, and antelope—have special pouches in which digestion is aided by bacterial action and completed by later chewing of the regurgitated mass before it is finally passed on to the stomach.

The herding habit has its advantages, too, comparable to that of a wide-sweeping mower over a hand-sickle. It enables the group to spread out over the range as it moves along. But this habit also affords the protection of numbers and of maneuver. On one occasion I visited one of the few bison reserves with a ranger. As our car slowly approached the herd, so gradually that we were scarcely aware of any other than normal movement, the cows and heifers formed into a double crescent with the calves enclosed. Presently the solitary bull took his position at one end of the crescent, whereupon our guide suggested that it was time to leave.

Sheer numbers of the group increase the chance for survival, as they do for schools of small fish in their voracious environment. Numbers also have a selective value, since the weaklings and stragglers are most vulnerable to carnivores, while the more vigorous and active tend to escape and reproduce.

One of the remarkable results of evolution in Africa is the survival of numerous species of antelopes, side by side. This has recently been explained by the preference of each species of antelope for a particular species of grass, thus reducing the intensity of competition among them.

Whether we consider such evidence of evolution as we have, or merely observe what happens to an abandoned field or road, we are impressed by the energy with which plants and animals take advantage of every opportunity to make a living. Because woody plants are more readily preserved than grasses and other herbs we know more about forests of the past than we do about ancient grasslands. But once the grasses had developed and came to occupy areas unsuited to forest the animal kingdom moved in to occupy and make use of them.

Most conspicuous among these invaders were the ancestors of grazing mammals. In the absence of arboreal shelter smaller mammals and reptiles were obliged to find underground homes, for both safety and shelter against the rigor of a continental climate. The same was true of insect and other invertebrate life. Often sustenance as well as shelter was provided by the dense network of fibrous roots and underground storage organs of the vegetation. But many of these subterranean dwellers emerged to feed upon green herbage, thus competing with the larger mammals for forage.

By no means were all of the gradually developing grassland fauna vegetarian. The plant-eaters, from the larger mammals to the insects, were a rich source of protein food. Everywhere they were present carnivores followed, notably members of the canine group and in places such cats as the lion. Many of these flesh-eaters had their favorite menus. Others were catholic, taking what they could get.

Essential to this intricate web of eaten and eater, plant, vegetarian, and carnivore were the users of dead waste. These were the insects and other invertebrates, fungi, and bacteria that returned nutrients to soil and air to continue the operation of the community. Step by step, in the course of obtaining the materials and energy for their own survival they oxidized the complex organic carbon compounds (chiefly proteins, carbohydrates, and fats) left as residue by plant and animal activities. This has been essential, for the raw materials which green plants draw in from earth and air are relatively simple compounds of oxygen with other nutrient elements.

Another extremely important service rendered to the community by microscopic forms of life has been the fixation of nitrogen from the air into simple compounds which plant roots could absorb for use in the manufacture of proteins. This is work which requires, as all work must, a source of energy. Some bacteria obtain it from dead material in the soil. Others get it by a kind of fair exchange with plants of the legume (clover and bean) family within whose roots they find harbor. In return for carbohydrates from the host, they supply nitrogen for its use.

The minerals that compose grassland soil are not of themselves rich

Bunch grasses in zone between tallgrass prairie and shortgrass plains, Nebraska Sand Hills.

in nitrogen compounds. I recall a distinguished plant physiologist who expressed his inability to understand the high concentration of nitrogen in prairie soils until a student from the West reminded him that, in addition to the conspicuous grasses, the prairies of Nebraska harbored nearly a hundred species of legumes. In the dryer shortgrass plains beyond, fertile except for the scarcity of water, nitrogen fixation is largely carried on by bacteria living free in the soil.

The grasslands of the world have developed into remarkably complex and beautifully interwoven systems, living on the current budget of solar energy and available materials, generally sustaining the maximum abundance of life possible under natural conditions.

Although much of the North American grassland had suffered from the impact of what we call civilization before it was studied critically by naturalists, there is ample evidence of its enormous richness and variety.

Continuous interior grassland occupies a strip varying from five hundred to one thousand miles wide east and west and more than two thousand miles in length north and south in North America. West of this are other great areas, interrupted by desert and mountain communities. All told, an enormous range of climatic conditions is represented, covered by the blanket term "continental" in distinction to those more humid climates known as "oceanic."

At the eastern limits where tallgrasses dominate, rainfall and evaporation are fairly balanced. Westward the gradient drops sharply, the drying power of the air rising, and the rainfall diminishing. From south to north mean annual temperatures drop and length of growing season diminishes. Neglecting differences in altitude, spring comes approximately a day later for each fifteen miles north while mean annual temperature drops roughly one degree Centigrade for each degree of latitude.

Thus at its margins the main body of grassland intermingles with very different communities in different directions—deciduous forest in the east, aspen parkland to the north, mountain foothill woodland to the west, scrub and desert southward. This naturally favors different groups of animals, mammals, birds, reptiles, and insects able to take advantage of the variety so afforded.

Of the two great dominant grazing animals it is estimated that the original population—that is before European invasion—was nearly equal. Although their ranges overlapped, some forty-five millions of bison were mainly toward the east, a similar number of antelope in the dryer western area. Both species took advantage of the growing season, moving with it north and south.

The immense populations of smaller forms and plants adjust themselves in various ways to the vast range of conditions. Rodents and reptiles, becoming dormant in the forty-degree range of temperature, retire to underground shelter, many of the rodents with stores of winter feed. Wolves, foxes, and cats can change their insulating coats with the seasons, while birds can migrate or find winter shelter. Insects, most highly developed and specialized of invertebrates, have complicated life cycles that enable them to remain inactive during unfavorable times.

Even so, drought and extreme cold often resulted in disaster. Populations fluctuated, as they have for all animal life. Tradition has it that the bison in what is now Illinois were virtually wiped out by a blizzard in Revolutionary times, several decades after the last authentic record of this noble beast in Ohio (where prairie outliers existed).

In the absence of man, animal populations have strong recuperative power. But when he appears, even at a primitive level of culture, the picture changes. There is now good evidence that the larger animals of postglacial time—elephant, camel, and horse—survived in America until they encountered Stone Age man.

Fortunately there have been studies of the rapidly disappearing natural grasslands, especially during the past three-quarters of a century. Though much more needs to be known about them, the information we do have gives us some important clues to processes that kept these areas functioning through millions of years, in contrast to the shifting impermanence of a few thousand years of human empire.

The remarkable network of animal life which we have so briefly sketched has been sustained by a beautifully integrated pattern of vegetation. Far from being a monotonous expanse of grasses, the prairie and dryer shortgrass were rich in plant species. Developing late in geological history as they did, it is not surprising that they were colonized by highly specialized and relatively youthful products of plant evolution.

In contrast to the survivors of more ancient families, represented by the few species uniquely fitted to survive, the newer groups display a great variety of kinds and individuals. It was undoubtedly this versatility which enabled them to adjust to changing conditions and compete effectively with forms now extinct.

A fair sample—often as little as an acre—of the most humid tall-grass prairie may contain as many as 250 different species of flowering plants, including the grasses, while the entire flora of these communities is of course much greater. In the dryer more severe habitat of North America known as the Plains, between 50 and 75 species are typical of study areas, while some 120 species have been listed as occurring familiarly in one or another phase of this vast community.

Only the most careless observer could miss the variety and beauty of the landscapes thus made possible. From early spring until frost there are changing waves of color and texture as the foliage, flower, and fruit of each of the many kinds of plants take their brief turn on parade. They never seem still, thanks to the constant moving of unchecked air currents. Even in winter it could be said: "As I looked about me I felt that the grass was the country. The red of the grass made all the prairie the color of winestains, or of certain seaweeds when they are first washed up. And there was so much motion in it: the whole country seemed, somehow, to be running."

Dominating this wealth of life are members of three families, young in the calendar of evolution and, world over, richest in number of species—grasses, composites, and legumes. Only the orchids, more at home in the tropics, yet not entirely absent here, rival them in variety. Members of more ancient groups are rare in the grasslands, the cone-bearing pines and junipers occurring as individuals or scattered stands near the mountain foothills. In moister sites such as canyon bottoms or temporary pools (known as buffalo wallows in Oklahoma) ferns and buttercups represent more primitive survivors.

The relative youth of grassland families has a reasonable enough explanation. About thirty million years ago, the last one thousandth or less of earth time, a great cycle of uplift began, resulting in the formation of mountain chains in Asia and the Americas, and of vast interior plateaus. Previously, earth climates had been more uniform, moister, and more genial than they are now. The gradual shutting off of immense areas of continental interiors from their previous sources of oceanic moisture opened these areas to nascent species, plastic enough to adapt themselves to dryer and harsher conditions.

Where grasses and other herbs could thrive there were few situations favorable to their preservation as fossils, for these are found chiefly in

Ungrazed native prairie at contact with Black Jack Cross-Timbers growing on sandy soil.

Wall of sumac at contact between prairie and valley woodland, Nebraska.

water-laid deposits. Nor are such plants so likely to become fossilized as the woodier kinds. Yet their remains do turn up, for instance in Kansas, where they clearly trace back to the fairly recent period of Tertiary uplift.

The old saying of classical physics, that nature abhors a vacuum, has its counterpart in biology. As gases, given the opportunity, press into empty space, so living organisms tend to crowd into any suitable niches that open up. So a whole complex of new and venturesome forms came to occupy the continental interiors slowly in terms of human experience, but rapidly in the calendar of evolutionary change.

Perhaps the most remarkable feature of the resulting vegetation is its amazing resilience. The climates to which it has become fitted are not only more severe than those prevailing during most of geological time but are marked by recurring crises. Beyond the sharp contrasts of day and night and seasons of the year are the longer ordeals of drought. Interspersed among times of adequate moisture, dry years tend to come in groups that may extend from a year or two to a decade or more.

Such emergencies require powerful defenses. Beyond those of individual plant structure and behavior is the more profound resource afforded by the rich variety of species. An army that relies upon a single instrument of warfare, or a community whose economy rests upon a single activity, is clearly vulnerable. Strength depends upon having more than one resource to deploy as new situations arise. Survival is keyed to alternatives.

As evidence of the sturdy equipment of the grassland we have not only the changing panoply throughout a single season but the apparent dominance during different years of very different groups of species. As conditions change some kinds of plants simply recede, not dying but merely remaining quiescent, showing slight growth if any, and often not producing flower and fruit. Others which have previously seemed absent or inconspicuous burgeon forth in response to a phase of climate or other circumstances favoring them.

The great drought of the 1930's, compounded by heavy pressure from man and his domestic animals, led to extreme changes. These, and the subsequent recovery with the waning of the drought have been skillfully observed and recorded, confirming the remarkable vitality and resilience of grassland in the face of extremes. The pattern of this difficult environment is one of the facts of life to be reckoned with wherever man attempts to use it. Surely the means by which plant and animal life have succeeded in meeting this challenge afford a model to be considered, in any sound economy of the continental interiors.

chapter six

The Grasses Themselves

GRANTING the rich panoply of plant species that make up the grasslands, especially in their less arid phases, it is the grass family which dominates the scene. To say this is not to overlook the versatility of this newcomer among flowering plants, for it is represented in forest, marsh, and desert as well as it is in the fields and gardens of man.

The grasses of the world are grouped into fewer than a score of tribes, containing over 500 genera, these again divided into some 4,500 species. In total number of individuals they probably exceed any other group of plants. The great woody bamboos may reach a height of a hundred feet, while there are some species of grass that are not more than an inch tall.

It is believed by specialists that the bamboos are to be reckoned among the most primitive of grasses and that, like the palms, they are the off-shoot of lily-like ancestors. This judgment rests upon the (often obscure) three-parted arrangement of their flowers, and the fact that the veins of their leaves are parallel instead of forming a network such as we see in maple and rose.

The more picturesque and useful grasses can be identified by ranchmen, gardeners, and the makers of lawn and golf green. But most grasses look alike to the average person, or enough so to discourage closer acquaintance. The slender upright blades and stalks reveal their differences only to close inspection, often requiring magnification by handlens or microscope. Seen thus they reveal details of considerable beauty such as delicate hairs, ribs, and toothed margins, over and above more obvious features of texture, geometry, and habit.

Useful as such vegetative characters may be, the critical identity of each grass species is often a difficult and highly technical problem. It is complicated not only by the extremely large number of species, but also by the usually tiny character and great simplicity of the grass flower, as compared with the more conspicuous flowers of other plants.

The success in the art of miniaturization of electrical circuits and other apparatus that has given us the transistor radio and computer is not a novelty without precedent. Nature has long exemplified it. Roaches and other primitive insects whose fossils date back to the Coal Age, some three hundred million years ago, spanned inches in length. The rapid evolution of insects, paralleling that of the flowering plants, has resulted not only in the largest single class of living organisms—some million or so species—but in a remarkable reduction in size of many of them. A good example are the pestiferous midges, appropriately called the No-See-Ums by the Indians of the North Woods.

The synchronized development of flowering plants and insects has involved many delicate interrelationships, one of them being the role of insects in the pollination of flowers. From this necessity, however, the grasses have been exempt. The attractions of size, color, and form so essential in flowers served by insects are superfluous in plants whose pollen is distributed by wind. A brief exposure of the organs producing and receiving the abundant dusty pollen is all that is necessary.

In grasses the showy petals and floral scents of insect-pollinated flowers have been dispensed with. The individual flowers are tiny, their essential organs enclosed in scales which open only long enough to permit pollination by the wind. In turn these flowers are grouped into spikelets, or closely packed vertical units containing sometimes one, more often several, florets. These spikelets form clusters, some compact like the head of wheat, in other grasses delicately branched, an invitation to the ministering breezes. (Wheat incidentally, being self-fertilized, is not handicapped by the tight arrangement of its flower clusters that excludes pollen from outside.)

Considering the difficulty to us as observers that results from the miniaturization of the grass flower, it may seem strange to call this organ simplified. Simplicity, however, is a two-edged concept. A shift made from a flour sack may be called simple. So may a highly sophisticated Paris creation, the product of skillful elimination and artistic design. An elaborate "fussy" gown can be thrown together without much thought and betray that fact. Whether we speak of the evolution of dress, architecture, or organic life, the net effect of functional compulsion and fitness seems to be a stripping down to essentials. Whatever the vagaries of human design over and above these essentials, or of the costly trial and error in organic evolution, the end results show a remarkable economy.

The derived simplicity of the grasses is evident in their fruits as well as the flowers that produce them, a fortunate circumstance for man. Each fruit contains a single seed, with the coats of fruit and seed fused into a single usually thin membrane; or, less frequently, it may be equipped with hooks or plumes to make possible its spread by animals or wind.

Within this covering is contained the embryo plant of the new generation, nested in a nutrient store of protein, carbohydrates, vitamins, digestive juices, and often oil. With the ripening of this remarkable package, neatly and completely packed for survival, the drying and opening of the chaffy scales that have enclosed the flower release the fruit, or grain as we call it. The ancient flail and our modern power-driven grain separators merely serve to speed up the process of nature, using wind (today from fans) to drive off the chaffy material.

Even before the domestication of our cereal grasses with their large grains the grains of wild species of grass were collected for food. The northern Plains Indians still use paddles to sweep wild rice into their canoes. This particular grain can be boiled and eaten without other treatment. On the arid island of Tiburón in the Gulf of California where agriculture was impossible I have seen a grinding stone which had been left in a cave by the aboriginal people who were long since gone. Obviously it was used to reduce the hard grains of grasses and wild seeds of other plants to meal. The well-balanced ration within the grass fruit has served generations of humans and still longer generations of other animals, as it has served to nourish the initial growth of the embryo plants for whose use it evolved and is so admirably fitted.

Small nutritious seeds of the smartweed and pigweed families as well as the larger fruits of the oak can be ground into flour, and still are where other foods are scarce. Nor are all cereal fruits as large as our

Wild barley.

wheat, rye, barley, and maize. In India and elsewhere the tiny grains of various grasses known as millets are an important source of food. These are grown in western lands chiefly for poultry feed and forage. But it was the domestication and processing of the larger grains that really liberated man from the irksome search for wild food sources that made it impossible to find time for much else.

The continuing search for traces of the earliest cereal culture is one of the many challenging problems of archaeology. In these investigations no clue can be neglected. Charred or dried grains, sickles and grinders, storage pits and dumps, art, legend, and word roots that have been preserved in the evolution of language all contribute to our knowledge. So too does the elusive quest for places of origin and centers of dispersal of original wild ancestors and nearest of kin of our cereals and other useful plants. The long time that has elapsed and the great changes that have taken place since early domestication of wheat, rice, and maize make this search a difficult one.

Near relatives of wheat grow wild in Palestine, of maize in Central America, but their actual prototypes have vanished into the shadows of time past. Our Indian corn is so modified by man that, as the late Henry Wallace said, this plant would probably not survive the last man by more than a few years. Above the bed of a lake that dried up centuries ago, Bat Cave in western New Mexico contains a heap of corn cobs and other rubbish several feet thick. Radiocarbon dates show that Indians occupied this cave between 4,000 and 2,100 years ago. Few of the cobs are larger than one's thumb. The giant ears grown today, ten inches long and four inches in diameter, are testimony of what man has wrought from primitive beginnings.

In recent decades new refinements have come into the search for knowledge. Reconstruction of the past is no exception. Archaeology in its quest for origins uses instruments that range from bulldozer to alidade, sieve, tweezers, and microscope, along with delicate devices of the physical laboratory. Willard Libby's great discovery that the rate of radioactive decay in the carbon of plant and animal remains can be used to date such materials with considerable accuracy back some thirty thousand years, has given us a calendar for the later stages of evolving human culture and attendant changes of environment. Within this span are included the final stages of the last great glaciation whose ice masses cleared the United States and northern Europe some ten thousand years ago. Previous estimates had ranged as far back as thirty thousand years.

Another technique, originating in Sweden and since perfected in many parts of the world, sheds light on the record of changing climate and vegetation, and upon the history of agriculture. Variously called pollen analysis, pollen statistics, or palynology, this method rests upon the circumstance that most of the dominant vegetation and economic plants are wind-pollinated. Not only do the forms of pollen grains reveal their origin, but in bogs, lake sediments, and very dry deposits they are beautifully preserved and can be recovered by taking cores.

In the laboratory these materials can be treated to concentrate the fossil pollen, which is then identified and tallied. When this is done such changes as the shift from cool coniferous to warmer deciduous forest, from forest to grassland, or from cool to warm desert can be identified. The changes in human land-use can also be traced in this way. In Denmark the Neolithic forest clearance, followed by cereal growing which gave way to weedy pastures, and the later return of forest is thus clearly recorded.

Among the cereals, and certainly among the entire family of grasses, maize is entitled to be considered a noble form. Distinguished in size and beauty, important as food for man and feed for his animals, and significant for its role in making possible the early civilizations of the western world, it is also one of the most highly specialized of grasses. This is attested by the separation of its sexual organs into the male tassel and female ear and by the transformations it has undergone at the hand of man, leading to its almost complete dependence upon him. In its rich variety and sensitive relationship to our own species, maize is comparable to our inseparable companion among animals, the dog.

Since maize is unknown in the wild state much study has been given to its origins. It does have close relatives among the native flora of Middle America and can interbreed with one of them, *Tripsacum dactyloides* or Eastern Grama Grass. It also resembles the Mexican *Euchlena* known as Teosinte, often suggested as one of its ancestors because of its tassel and large grains. Since the Teosinte is still cultivated, it seemed reasonable to suppose that maize originated in a prehistoric garden through hybridization or another genetic event. To support this idea there are some impressive technical data.

Then, beginning in 1948, the two-hundred-odd feet of lake sediment on which Mexico City rests was studied for its content of fossil pollen. Far down in these deposits, long antedating the presence of man, pollen closely resembling that of maize was discovered and turned over to an impartial laboratory for critical examination. (Too often reports of finds of prehistoric material, especially those that controvert accepted ideas, have led to more heat than light. The first report of missile points associated with an extinct species of bison was received with scorn, though a score of years later the coexistence of hunters with vanished animals of the glacial period in America was amply confirmed. On the other hand, the sensational Swanscombe skull, purporting to be that of a primitive human, turned out to be a contrived fake.) The ancient grass pollen far below the levels of human presence in Mexico was finally proved to be that of *Zea mays*. In the words of the distinguished scientist, Paul Mangelsdorf, who had believed this plant to be a hybrid of closely related wild species and whose generous reception of contrary evidence is exemplary, "the ancestor of maize was maize."

To follow these comments on the reproductive features of the grasses, culminating in the large nutritious fruits that have been so essential to the emergence of civilized man, there remain other qualities of this remarkable family of plants that have played a vital role from still earlier stages of the human adventure. These are the features of the vegetative shoot—stem and foliage—that are so perfectly adapted to sustain the great fauna of grazing animals that has developed.

What we might well call the "grassiness" of the grass plant has been of peculiar importance to organic evolution and to that of the total landscape. It enabled this group of plants to form vast expanses of ground cover where climate was unfavorable to forest and to maintain itself while feeding great herds and the accompanying complex of animal life, vertebrate and invertebrate, that could not conceivably have developed in its absence.

The slender, nearly vertical shoots and the fibrous roots of grasses make possible the densely crowded firm growth we call sod or turf. Thanks to this development, soil is formed and stabilized and maximum use is made of space, sun, water, and minerals. Unlike the more primitive fern body and that of most broad-leaved flowering plants whose delicate growing tissues are at the exposed tip of leaf or shoot, those of the typical grasses are down within the coronet of blade-like leaves until flowering time. Here they are protected from all but the closest cropping, such as occurs when pasture or range is overgrazed.

Furthermore, unlike the leaves of such familiar plants as the rose and tomato, those of the grasses—their blades—continue to grow from the

Wild prairie grass in wind, south of Lincoln, Nebraska.

base, so that when the tip is removed by teeth or mower, growth continues as it does in our hair after a visit to the barber. Thus in addition to the growing point of the shoot, which has produced whatever stem there may be and will eventually produce flower and fruit, the typical grasses that serve for forage continue to produce leaf tissue throughout the growing season.

It is this remarkable property that has made possible the evolution of the immense herds of grazing mammals and the concomitant wealth of animal life that occupies the less than humid portions of earth. A further characteristic, neither limited to grasses nor possessed by all of them, has served powerfully in the formation of continuous ground cover of turf. This is the habit of forming buds at the base of the shoot. These buds, growing laterally above the ground in sand-binding grasses, and below it in the aggressive Johnson grass, develop into shoots that strike root and emerge into the air and form clumps about their original parent plant.

In this way many grasses are able to multiply even if their fruits fail to develop or are bitten off during the brief period when they, or the flowers that produce them, are exposed. Various circumstances known or as yet unknown may inhibit flowering, sometimes for long periods, without lessening the capacity of perennial grasses to survive. Among the bamboos, years may elapse between seed years. When they do occur the nutritious grains afford a rich feast for birds. Or if, in the prairie, years pass without fire, growth and flowering may be suppressed. The community becomes, in a sense, muscle-bound by its own success in drawing upon the nutrients of the soil. In the dry air these accumulate in dead, undecayed litter. When the inevitable fire sweeps across, this debris is converted into soluble ash, releasing the bound minerals, renewing a vigorous growth and flowering for the next season.

Fire, like grazing, is a normal part of the grassland regime. Only when either of these two events becomes too frequent or intense is the community depressed, changing its composition and lowering its productiveness.

Both before and after the development of genetics man produced many types of cultivated plants, including the grasses. At first by selection, later by controlled breeding, he developed forms suited to his needs by chemistry, fitness to different soils and climates, and resistance to diseases. But as in many other respects, his efforts were anticipated in the long slow course of natural variation and elimination.

A native species of the valuable grama grass ranges north and south through the United States, where growing seasons vary from 100 to 320 days. In the same span the summer day is longer and night briefer as one moves from Texas to North Dakota. When samples of this species of grass are collected at points along the north-south line and brought into the laboratory for testing, each is found to reflect the conditions of its home. Those from the South with its long growing season take longer to mature. Those from the North respond best to long intervals of light. These characteristics are fixed in inheritance.

More than this, when individuals of the same species are gathered from the same patch of prairie and tested under controlled conditions, they are found to differ in their genetic make-up, responding variously to the factors of environment. Even plants that grow side by side and look alike reflect the plasticity which in the long past has enabled their kind to adjust to the fluctuations so inevitable in any environment.

What we would call resourcefulness in a conscious being has its counterpart in the resilience of the grass family. Beyond that shown by individual species, this quality is enhanced by the wide range of fitness among different species.

Despite the scarcity of natural stands of grassland, enough remained to have been studied during the disastrous drought of the 1930's and the subsequent recovery. As the succession of dry years became more intense in its effect, the short grasses of the semiarid high plains shifted eastward at the expense of the more luxuriant taller kinds of the subhumid prairies. Where the effects of drought had been aggravated by abuse and over-grazing, weedy annuals and such plants as cactus were among the invaders. Later, as drought receded and conditions became more normal this process reversed itself. The taller grasses that had been reduced to as little as 10 percent of the visible cover in 1932 gradually regained their dominant position by the 1950's.

The actual mechanism of this process was by no means simple. Less resistant individuals died, leaving bare spaces open to seed blown in from the West. Others, sometimes by virtue of deeper roots, survived in a dormant state. With recovery, the taller species regained their advantage in the competition for light, shading out the shorter invaders. But whatever the processes, the observations yielded a superb demonstration of the inherent vigor and resilience of natural communities.

To this catalog of the remarkable properties of the grasses we should add its chemical resources and physical textures. The aromatic lemon grasses that flourish in warm climates are a source of citronella oil, used as a mosquito repellent before the invention of synthetic commercial products. Farther north the sweet or vanilla grass was gathered by the Indians and woven into fragrant baskets. Its near relative, called Holy Grass in Europe, was strewn as a carpet at church doors in times of religious festival, while it was probably the American species which, for a similar reason, was called Roman Catholic Grass. This name is recorded in early accounts of the Sandusky region in Ohio, where Willa Cather laid the opening scene of *Death Comes to the Archbishop*.

Man has developed many uses for the fibrous structure of grasses, most notably perhaps those of the woody bamboo. Thatch, clothing, mats, basketry, and paper have all made use of appropriate grasses in their manufacture. The common reed, so abundant in coastal and inland marshes, has served for the building of huts and the making of arrow shafts. Harvested in November, it can be shaped into beautiful lettering pens.

In addition to the rich store of nutrients in grass fruits that we have noted, much could be said of those in stem and leaf. Such a catalog would include the sugars of cane and sorghum stems as well as the cellulose in forage grasses which ruminants are specially equipped to convert into sugars. In contrast to the cultivated grasses used for hay, which must be harvested just at the proper time to preserve their value, those of the high plains nourished the bison throughout the year as they do modern range cattle because of their ability to cure without loss of food content.

chapter seven

Savanna and Scrub

THE ceaseless activity within the grassland is matched at its borders. Just as the plants and animals within it quickly take advantage of favorable shifts in critical conditions to invade territory previously barred to them, so the living communities surrounding the grassland formations advance in response to opportunity or retreat under pressure.

Some broad, some narrow, these dynamic zones of tension are marked by mixtures of the life-forms of the adjacent communities. Those that separate the moister prairies from the more arid steppes consist of clumps of medium height and occasionally of the taller prairie plants, scattered through a carpet of the shorter grasses. Variously known as midgrass or mixed prairies, their appearance responds to slight differences in soil, slope, and moisture.

Spanning great reaches of continental climate and reflecting a great range of conditions, at their margins the grasslands compete with widely different types of neighboring community. Except where they shade directly into true desert, their chief opponents in the struggle for living

77

space are woody plants. Normally, at its dryer margins grassland encounters and mingles with scrub, a belt or zone of low woody plants
without proper trunks which branch out at the ground. Technically these
are called shrubs to distinguish them from trees. As scrub ventures into
still dryer conditions it gradually yields to true desert, in our own Southwest for example.

On its more genial boundaries the grassland comes into competition
with forest. Where this contact is along wooded stream courses or can-
yons it is abrupt, marked by a narrow band of venturesome shrubs that
advances or retreats from its forest stronghold as moisture, fire, or other
circumstances may dictate. Like the scouting cavalry or advance guard
of an army, the sumac, wild plum, vines, and briars at the valley margins
in Kansas and Nebraska penetrate the prairie in favorable times, give
way to the upland grasses and forbs under stress.

Even within the prairie the contest goes on. In rolling country one
may see small thickets—called "pockets" by the natives—of wild plum,
coralberry, or other dwarfed shrubs. These are most frequent where
shallow depressions on a gentle slope tend to result in patches of somewhat moister soils. Where moisture supply is critical, almost unbelievably
slight differences in level can be important. Corn thrives on low hills or
ridges along the moist Atlantic coast, as the Indians taught the Pilgrims;
in the dryer prairie states its chance to germinate and grow is much better
if the seeds are planted in shallow pits or furrows. There, wheat and other
grasses may be visibly taller and greener in tracks left by wagon wheels.

On a much grander scale, on all the continents where moisture permits,
the zones of contest are savannas. Most extensive in Africa where they
boast a rich fauna of wild game, their Spanish name (*savana*) derives
from a West Indian word *zabana*. Originally applied to tropical or subtropical grassy plains with scattered trees, or even with none, its use has
been expanded to designate open landscapes of trees and grasslands
wherever found.

It may refer to the broad plains of Africa, the hummock-dotted
marshes of Florida, the mesquite and short-grass of Texas, the grove-
land of Iowa, the oak openings of Ohio, or the aspen parkland of Canada.
In all of these situations trees, singly or in groups, are scattered, instead
of forming continuous forests.

Wherever they may be, whatever the plants that compose them, savannas have two very significant attributes. Once established in places where
tensions of climate or soil favor them, they are readily perpetuated.

Oak-grass savanna in California.

During dry seasons their grasses are vulnerable to fire, while the trees that are most frequently present can withstand it, although it hinders their reproduction. Fire, along with the presence of grazing animals from the adjacent true grassland, tends to discourage the spread of tree seedlings.

Yet there are instances, in the infinite complexity of living nature, in which animals promote the invasion of grassland by shrubs and small trees. On a small scale this is familiar to many householders who find young seedlings of oak or walnut in their lawns, courtesy of industrious squirrels who either absentmindedly or for more serious reasons fail to retrieve a bit of buried treasure.

In the Southwestern states a bean-bearing tree, the mesquite, has been expanding its range since the introduction of cattle. Although these beans are nutritious, their hard coats permit many to pass through the alimentary canal without damage, probably with improved power of germination. In the temporary cover of cattle droppings, mesquite has the advantage of a good start. Later it is protected by its thorns.

An important characteristic of savanna is recognized by naturalists and wildlife managers, who speak of "edge effect." Open grassy woodland or sparsely wooded grassland, containing, as it does, the plant life of two major communities, invites the presence of animals from both. Deer thrive where open areas are provided either by nature or man within otherwise unbroken forest. Quail and rabbit as well as songbirds and rodents find a more congenial home near the forest margins than within the deep woods, as both hunter and watcher soon discover. The transition zone between forest and grassland abounds in small game as well as fruits and nuts. Hazel, plum, grape, and apple (or their equivalents where these are not native) furnish food for man and beast.

That man's ancestry goes back to tree dwellers is no longer in doubt. His grasping hands, stereoscopic vision (so necessary to a climber in judging distance), and the habits of his nearest relatives in the animal kingdom all support this view. So too, do the facts of geological and climatic history, as far as they are understood. For the early stages in human, or prehuman, evolution took place in the comparatively genial climate of the early Tertiary, around fifty million years ago. At that time the earth was largely forest-clad. The vast continental uplift which brought about the drying and cooling that led gradually to the succession of ice ages and the expansion of continental grassland and desert, was just beginning.

Bertha Dutton

Tension zone between grass and trees, Cochise County, Arizona.

With the stubborn retreat of woodland and the opening up of the landscape came the opportunity to explore the developing savanna at the forest margin. The scattered trees still gave occasion to exercise the art of climbing. Their fruits, thanks to abundant sunshine, were more easily reached than those of the tall forest trees, which grow in deep shade, except at their tops. (The late Professor Chamberlain of Chicago became an expert with the rifle because, he said, often the only way he could collect flowers and fruits in the tropical forest was to shoot them down.)

The teeth of our precursors, like our own, were better suited to biting and grinding than to tearing. Without the aid of tools this meant a diet of fruits, roots, and nuts, supplemented by grubs and other invertebrates as well as the tender flesh of small birds and mammals. The rich store of flesh from the great herds of animals grazing in the open country beyond the savanna remained unavailable to the unarmed primate, except as tidbits rescued from vultures and other scavengers.

Savanna then, for more reasons than one, must have been the nursery of the humanoids, as the forest had been their cradle. It afforded free exit as they left the forest. It abounded in the kind of food they could gather and use, while its combination of trees and open space was an ideal gymnasium in which to rehearse the art of walking upright, while still practicing the ancestral skill of climbing.

Throughout succeeding millennia, as the use of fire and shaping of tools and weapons developed, the open grassy woodlands maintained their hospitality. Low-growing easily broken branches were an obvious source of fuel. What early tools were shaped from them we can only guess, since wood decays. But the use of digging stick, bow, and spear shaft that persists in modern times suggests that cleverness in the manufacture of flints may have been matched by skill in the working of useful items from wood. Even the steel-using settlers in our own Midwest chose sites where trees were available, partly because they thought the soil more fertile (which was not the case), but also because they needed fuel and building material.

Having preempted those parts of the prairie country where wood was available, these settlers laughed at the Scandinavian latecomers who were obliged to settle on the open grassland. The newer arrivals soon discovered that the tough prairie sod could be built into snug quarters, cool in summer and warm in winter, while the dried droppings of bison, later of cattle, furnished excellent fuel.

As recently as 1920 two of us enjoyed the hospitality of a remote prairie home. While our breakfast was being prepared over a fire of "chips" whose aroma is not unlike that of burning peat, our host showed us a snapshot of his fuel pile of the preceding autumn. It had been perhaps fifteen or twenty feet long and some twelve feet in height, and the picture showed a ladder leaning up against it. He told us that he had taken this photograph along on a visit to eastern relatives. A caller who saw it became quite excited, saying she had a question to ask if he did not mind. "What I don't understand," she gushed, "is how you get the cows up there." Without a smile he replied, "You see that ladder," leaving her more amazed than ever at the wonders of pioneer life.

In Africa the attempt to convert vast stretches of savanna from hunting territory to agriculture is more recent. It involves difficulties much greater than those encountered in temperate regions. Tropical soils deteriorate rapidly when robbed of their natural cover and exposed to sun and rain, becoming unsuitable for mass crop production.

This has given rise to sharp differences of opinion. Many naturalists familiar with Africa have been impressed with the high protein yield that would be possible under a system of controlled hunting of the great herds that thrive on the native vegetation of the African savanna plains. It is this belief and not only ethical, aesthetic, and scientific considerations that explains the widespread concern for the preservation of these magnificent groups of wildlife and the conditions they need to survive. Whether this concern can carry the day against our missionary zeal to mechanize the world and the infectious desire of undeveloped nations to imitate our way of life is now touch and go.

The strong warming and drying that marked the final retreat of continental glaciers made possible not only the increase of grasslands, but also that of the combination of grass and scattered trees at their peripheries which we call savanna. The archeological evidence shows this to have been a time of diffusion of the human race. The state of material culture being what it was, forest remained a serious obstacle to this diffusion. Open landscapes were not. The savannas, with their edge effect, furnished food from small game and plants. To people simply equipped and with little social organization, unable as yet to cope with the large game of the open grasslands, this was essential.

Where extensive areas of savanna plain developed, as in Africa, whether maintained later by fire or animal pressure, they came to support an abundance of larger game—browsers that fed on shrubs and trees as well as the grazers that depended upon herbage. In the course of time techniques were developed for harvesting this prolific source of protein food. Whether the insight afforded by science and the instruments of modern technology will be used to encourage the sustained harvest of this ancient resource or to supplant it with attempts at mass production of other crops remains to be seen. Odds seem to favor the latter course, be it wise or foolish.

Scrub—or woody landscape without trees—is open in the sense that man on foot can see the sky. It does not, however, invite easy travel unless paths are cut through it or fire destroys it. Somewhat more generously supplied with moisture than the desert it so frequently abuts, it shares the desert's ability to resist drought, even though more densely packed with vegetation. The shrubs that dominate it are equipped for survival in various ways. Their leaves may be leathery and coated wth wax or matted hair—adjustments to meet the drying power of air. Their leaves may be small and seasonal, dropping off and thus reducing water loss when this becomes a threat. Frequently the plants of the scrub are armed with thorns that make them inhospitable to all but such hardy browsers as sheep, goat, and camel.

On a large-scale map, scrub, like the adjoining desert, tends to show up toward the western and equatorward parts of the great land masses. This is true of the California chaparral, the garigue and maquis of the Mediterranean lands, and the thorn bush of Australia and Africa. The American motorist travelling from Laredo, Texas, toward Mexico City must pass through many miles of scrub before he reaches the tropical forests of the hot humid *tierra caliente* around Tamazunchale.

So far as the layman is concerned, scrub might as well be desert. The vast expanse of sagebrush in the Great Basin of Wyoming and Utah can, with equal ease, be called either scrub or cool desert. Only the spacing, wide or close, and the varying proportions of intermediate ground cover (grasses or water-storing, spiny desert plants) serve to make technical distinctions possible.

From this description one might conclude that the scrub community is well enough let alone by man. Such a judgment fails to allow for either man's enterprise or the grim pressures that stimulate it. The term "Maquis" (used first to designate the bandits of Corsica, later the French Underground of World War II), derives from the thorny scrub that has for centuries afforded a safe refuge for outlaws.

Following the workmanlike destruction of its ancient way of life by the Spaniards in the early sixteenth century, the population of central

Mexico dropped sharply. Many, however, managed to survive by fleeing into the northern scrub where there was little to tempt pursuit.

Water, though scarce, was available from scattered springs and certainly there was fuel enough. We still have proof of the remarkable skill of rural Mexicans in fashioning whatever is available into tools, utensils, and shelter. The same ingenuity must have gone into the search for food. The venturous gourmet will find for himself how thoroughly the edible resources of that country have been mined. Among the delicacies that will surprise and even please him are such items as plump and savory maguey worms and corn-smut and the egg masses of the water beetle. Granted, he might have to be fortified for his initial experiment with a touch of potent tequila. But he will soon find this superfluous.

Yet with all their enterprise in finding food, the life of refugees in the scrub could only have been one of hardship. Wherever food and water are scarce people will be sparse and scattered. And the inhabitants of preconquest America were handicapped in another respect when it came to utilizing areas of woody scrub. They lacked domestic forms of the Ovids—goats and sheep—notoriously able to thrive on this type of vegetation, and, curiously, often responsible for spreading it at the expense of more lush kinds of plant life. True, the prong-horned antelope, largest and fleetest denizen of scrub, can become a pet if caught young. But where food is scarce such specimens would be most unlikely to survive long in captivity (if indeed they could be induced to breed under such restraint).

None of the smaller animals of the scrub—jackrabbits, rats, birds, reptiles, and insects—lend themselves to the establishment of a productive animal industry. This development had to await the coming of the Europeans with their domestic cattle. In the Old World the goat had a particularly intimate and complex relation to the various types of scrub so characteristic of the Mediterranean region. Caricatured by us for its curious dietary habits such as eating the labels off tin cans and the wash off the line, its versatility is not entirely advantageous. Useful as it is for its yield of milk and flesh and its low cost of maintenance, it can be dangerous, like some of our modern engineering devices, unless properly controlled.

Prescientific man was often remarkably intuitive. Mohammed, for example, warned his followers that devils lurked under dirty fingernails. As for the goat, it is hardly an accident that the mischievous satyrs were pictured as resembling him, or that Satan was invested with a cloven hoof. Custom and ceremony preserved from the antique past and ranging from revelry to obscene rite celebrate the ambivalent relation of this animal to humanity.

Yet just as we accept a monthly death toll from the automobile so for centuries others have passively put up with the degradation of their landscape by a more ancient domestic utility—the goat. A few years ago a scholar from the Near East was telling of the rural troubles of his country, very accurately describing this kind of damage. Yet he was frankly surprised when the culprit was named to him. Fortunately not much testimony was required (his profession is the law) to convince him that indictment of the goat was in order.

Whether foraging on scant clumps of grass or browsing on the leaves and branches of open woodland, the goat can be highly destructive. He can stand on his hind feet or even climb on a leaning tree trunk to reach its twigs and branches. Since the shrubs with thick leathery leaves and thorns are more resistant to his attentions than more tender plants, the former tend somehow to survive and spread. One suspects that their initial advantage comes from his preference for other foods. Scrub springs up and grows when, so to speak, his back is turned. Meanwhile the production of more nutritious forage necessary for other forms of domestic animals suffers from his voracity. And man, at the top of the food pyramid, suffers in proportion. From Spain through Persia and along the north coast of Africa the presence of scrub in lands that were once more nutritiously clothed is eloquent testimony to the activity of this devilish yet useful animal.

We have seen the spread of mesquite savanna by cattle. One need not visit classic lands to observe invasion of grassy range by scrub because of animal activity. Some years ago our field group from Montana was working near West Yellowstone and noted that grass was being rapidly replaced by the less palatable sagebrush. This interesting, highly scented shrub was establishing itself upon mounds of bare soil made by burrowing gophers and ground squirrels.

The question naturally arose as to why this change was suddenly proceeding so vigorously. We learned that the ranchers were conducting a campaign of extermination against the coyote, using lethal cyanide bombs attached to bait. With the coyote disposed of there remained little check on gophers and ground squirrels. Since that time the economic wisdom of putting up with rodents instead of coyotes, trading good pasture for sagebrush in order to save the occasional lamb or calf crippled by birth defects from being eaten by coyotes, has been questioned. Stomach contents of coyotes show the bulk of their diet to consist of rodents and insects. In one district of Colorado at least, ranchers have decided to protect the coyote.

This is not to imply that sagebrush, where it occurs naturally, is useless. It affords a low-cost range for sheep, which like the prong-horn are able to browse upon it. It provided the wealth of Senator Warren of Wyoming, father-in-law of General Pershing. Old photographs taken on his ranch show only sagebrush and sheep as far as the eye could reach. The Senator was sometimes referred to as the greatest shepherd since Abraham.

The competition between grasses and woody plants, whether exemplified by savanna or in more arid climates by scrub, is a continuing and intriguing phenomenon.

chapter eight

Desert

TO get from Mexico City to Toluca which lies somewhat south of west, one must climb up through the *Desierta des Leones*—the Desert of the Lions. Unless forewarned, he will be surprised to find not an arid waste but a pleasant open forest of pine trees. Or if he is driving through the cool well-watered State of Maine he will be invited by roadside signs to visit the Desert of Maine. When he arrives, should curiosity be strong enough to loosen his purse for an admission fee, he will have the privilege of gazing upon an area of drifting sand. He will find it not too different from the great dunes near Provincetown on Cape Cod or those that border Lake Michigan on east and south.

Lieutenant Pike had little good to say of the vast region west of the Mississippi which he traveled. Until two or three generations of tough pioneers had developed a going if at times precarious economy within it, there were many who accepted his label, "The Great American Desert," as proper, although it included a great deal of fertile and productive land.

Among the laborsaving devices we love is the stereotype. Where desert is concerned two qualities symbolize it in the popular mind. One is sand, the other heat. The wind scarcely has time to smooth over the tracks left on location in the dunes of California before another gripping Saharan scene is ready to be filmed. Yet Lawrence of Arabia has vividly described the stretches of rock, gravel, and clay that pave the deserts of the Near East.

As to heat, assuredly one can encounter it, as he can sand, in many desert areas. But depending upon the time of day or year, he can as certainly shiver with piercing cold in the same locations. A third feature of the desert stereotype and in general a juster one (with exceptions already noted) is the lack of water. For in the great deserts of the world moisture is indubitably scarce. Yet even to this there are exceptions, for rain when it does come may be torrential, resulting in great, if short-lived, washes. Or rain may come at the wrong season of the year to be of much benefit to plant life.

There are other exceptions. Even in the dryest deserts enough water vapor may be present in the air to condense as dew during nocturnal cold. Nor is it easy to find a more descriptive term for the virtually lifeless streams which have been poisoned by the chemical wastes of civilization than "wet deserts."

All of which brings us to something of a paradox. Normally a particular landscape evokes reactions as diverse as those who look at it. Soldier, engineer, farmer, and artist each reads his own meaning into the same valley, plain, or hill and will describe it in his own vocabulary. With the desert the situation is reversed to a considerable degree. The same term is applied to situations that differ in many respects. That term, incidentally, is a word with few synonyms. Those for hill and valley can be numbered by the score.

Of Latin origin, the word "desert" has survived without much change in either the Romance languages or our own. Literally it means something disjoined, logical enough when applied to one who deserts his group or is deserted by it.

Modern German has two words, *die Wüste* (desert, wilderness) and *die Öde* (desert, solitude). The first is akin to our word "waste," the second implies emptiness as in the sad Wagnerian line *Öde ist das Meer.* Both are generously used to imply the disagreeable and inhospitable.

French and Spanish are quite direct. For both, the criterion of desert is the absence of a population, by implication one of human beings. The French *désert* being defined as *inhabité;* the Spanish *desierto* as *despoblado*.

A visitor, suddenly plumped down on the Speedway in Tucson or transported to the glittering twenty-four-hour-a-day, seven-day-a-week Strip in Las Vegas and told that he was in the midst of desert, would question his source of information or his wits. These spots are anything but depopulated. Even if he had the good fortune to visit the untouched desert with a naturalist friend he would find it, with rare exceptions, surprisingly well stocked with plant and animal life.

Even so, the common attribute of desert, whatever its cause or location, is the relative sparseness of the primary food producers—green plants—and consequently of the other forms of life that depend upon them, including man. A rough and ready test that reflects this characteristic is the wide spacing of the larger, dominant plants of the desert, or conversely the bare soil visible between them. Only for a brief period after the occasional season of rain is this open soil covered with a burst of annual plants. Elsewhere, as in forest or grassland, one sees bare soil only where there has been disturbance of the natural cover.

Space, so often the limiting factor in production, is not the problem in desert. Rather the restraint upon abundant life must be sought in dearth of moisture, the chemical composition of the soil, or some physical quality such as soil instability. Where these difficulties can be overcome, either by man or nature, space ceases to be a negligible asset and becomes a major one. Properly subsidized the desert may be made to teem with life. Underground water from springs or wells provides a subsidy to oases, while the local concentration of animal and plant residues maintains the supply of nutrients. Streams bringing in water and fertile silt from moister sources render a similar service to their irrigated valleys.

In the case of desert resorts the subsidy is a more conventional one, taking the form of cash accumulated elsewhere and brought in by seekers of sunshine or excitement. With such golden magic, water and other facilities can be made available. Through modern transportation by rail, highway, and air it is possible to offset the deficiencies of deserts where the cost seems justified for military reasons or for the exploitation of valuable mineral resources. Public conscience, still ineffectual in preventing war, at least requires the testing of atomic explosives to be re-

Wide-spaced desert perennials with patches of grass due to recent rain, Baja California.

Flowering yucca and desert shrubs, Baja California.

Desert in bloom after rain, infrequent and unpredictable, Baja California.

stricted to remote unpopulated areas. To this end, great governments move costly supplies, equipment, and men into the deserts of Africa, Eurasia, and North America.

By their very lack of hospitality deserts have traditionally offered sanctuary to souls in flight from the distractions and oppressions of a world too much with them. The eremites sought to escape temptation— doubtless with variable success—and to find solitude for contemplation there. Others have sought, within the desert, to insulate themselves against intolerance. Notable among these have been the Latter Day Saints or Mormons under the remarkable leadership of Brigham Young.

This great Mormon autocrat was an empire builder in the true sense. Unlike the ruthless captains and swivel-chair tyrants to whom we apply that term he created a cooperative social and economic system. My first measure of his greatness came during the Depression of the 1930's, when I left the region of urban shantytowns and bread lines and passed long heaps of rotting wheat beside the railroad, en route to Salt Lake City.

Here in the midst of unquestionable desert there were plenty of people, but no shacks, no bread lines. There was food and work for all. Here and there a vacant lot revealed the desert conditions that had prevailed before mountain water had been harnessed by the pioneers. On either side of it were lush green lawns, eloquent testimony to powerful leadership and dedicated, organized enterprise.

Seeing these things for the first time was an experience never to be forgotten, one that raised an inevitable question. "How," I asked a Mormon friend, "could Brigham Young have had any conception of the possibilities of this desolate land? And how could he have led his people on the long and weary way to it?"

"I used to wonder about these things too," was his reply, "and when I was a child I was told that the faithful were guided here by a pillar of cloud by day, a pillar of fire by night. But since I have grown up I have come to suspect that old Jim Bridger had a hell of a lot to do with it."

Bridger, fur trader and guide to exploring expeditions, knew the mountain West and its resources. He may have been the first white man to see the Great Salt Lake. Although he later served as guide to a military expedition against the Mormons, his early reports influenced Brigham Young in selecting his destination.

The desert around Salt Lake City is an expression of profound climatic change rather than of merely local conditions such as those responsible for the "Desert" of Maine. High around the valley run successive rim-lines of what was not too many thousands of years ago a vast freshwater lake. With the waning of the last great glaciation the rising temperature, diminished rainfall, and increasing evaporation drove the zones of moisture, snow, and forest up out of the valley into the mountains. From these higher sources water still ran down, but in the dryer air much of it was lost on the way. At best the supply would not have been enough to maintain the lake level against loss by evaporation.

Just as heated brine left uncovered becomes thicker, so the solution of minerals very dilute in the original high-level freshwater lake became more concentrated as the water dried down. Eventually what remained was—and is—saltier than the sea. These saline or alkaline lakes are features of the world's great climatic deserts. Added to other evidence, they justify our belief that these deserts are the product of changes that in the measure of geological time are fairly recent.

If as one flies from Alaska his plane stops at Whitehorse in the Canadian Yukon, he will see the shore lines of vanished lakes on the hillside across from the landing field. The traveler driving south from the Tetons and passing through Logan, Utah, will see terraces beautifully preserved as though etched by engineering calculation. The dust of caves, now high above the valley floor where Lake Winnemucca lies in Nevada, contains evidence not only of former habitation and higher lake levels but of more humid climate than that of today. And in the Mohave Desert where the mineral residue from evaporation is now profitably mined, under some ninety feet of saline sediment, at a level dated about ten thousand years ago, is evidence of open woodland predating the present austere desert.

Whether we examine the ancient shorelines above the basin in which Mexico City lies or organic and cultural remains in the Sahara the same record of gradual desiccation appears. We must, however, as in any attempt to reconstruct the past, proceed cautiously, whether dealing with a crime of man or an episode in nature. We know that earth's climates have been for the most part more equable and hospitable than at present, due in part at least to low land relief and high proportion of water to land. But there have been several periods of revolution, marked by continental uplift and mountain building. Whether there were accompanying changes in the intensity of radiation from the sun is not known. But the increase in both glaciers and deserts during long periods of revolution seems well established.

Saguaro (giant cactus) desert, Arizona.

This in itself presents an intriguing paradox. The record left by microscopic plant remains, notably pollen, indicates that during the height of glaciation deserts shrank and became more humid while lakes far beyond the ice margin were full. Then, as the continental and alpine glaciers shrank, the deserts expanded and the lakes dried up. Certainly the formation of great mountain ranges created a barrier against moist winds from the ocean, lessening rainfall in the sheltered interior. There is little doubt that these circumstances, starting in mid-Tertiary some sixteen million years ago, initiated the beginning of desert and grassland climates and the evolution of their characteristic plants and animals.

The subsequent development of massive glaciation is more difficult to explain. Merely to invoke a general cooling is scarcely enough, for there must be an extraordinary supply of moisture as well and this has to come from the oceans. During the height of the last glaciation, sea level was some two to three hundred feet lower than at present. Northern Greenland is dry. Here, despite the cold, there is no glacial ice. Instead the great ice cap covers the southern portion which receives abundant snow. In our own Rockies, the persistence of alpine snow banks depends upon the amount of winter snowfall at least as much as upon the amount of summer heat.

These observations suggest that playing upon the rugged pattern of mountain chains and interior plateaus there were changes in the amount of energy received from the sun. As it increased, more water was drawn from the seas by evaporation, leading to greater snowfall on mountain heights and polar regions reached by moist air masses. In time the accumulation of snow, converted by its own pressure into ice, may have reached a point where not even the increased solar heat was sufficient to check it. If this were true, the growing ice masses, impelled by their own weight, would begin to spread and grind their way down and out onto lower terrain. Beyond the ice margins, where the increased precipitation came as rainfall, lakes would fill and deserts shrink.

Such an explanation has the curious effect of invoking not less, but greater solar heat as having triggered an age of ice. We know from the fossil record of land life and marine deposits that temperatures on land and sea were lower during the times of the great glaciers. The presence of so much ice certainly must have had a refrigerating effect, but to what degree, if any, a change in the sun's behavior may have been involved is not yet clear.

We do know that there were four major ice advances during the past million or so years, separated by intervals much like the present. There is in fact a growing belief that we are in not a post- but an interglacial interval at the present time. The indubitable pulsations between heat and cold, moisture and dryness, that have accompanied glacial advance and retreat are still not explained. Ice can evaporate in dry air as well as melt from warmth. As glaciers grew at the expense of the seas, the relative elevation of land increased and with it the expanse of dry continental climate.

Meanwhile the cold of the vast ice masses shifted storm tracks toward the equator. (Cold Canadian air of today wrings moisture from the warm wet air of the Gulf of Mexico.) Thus the glaciers were no longer nourished, while the dry air over them may have aided the sun's warmth in their dissolution. Could it be that the great continental glaciers suffered in some measure at least from their own success?

This would be curious indeed, yet not without precedent in nature. Great surges in population create tensions which are followed by shrinkage. Massive mountains, pushed up by internal stresses, seem to us eternal yet are vulnerable to the force of gravity. Exposed to heat and cold, wind and rain, their surface materials become loosened and are blown, washed, or simply rolled down to a position of repose. In a valley of the Wasatch mountains, cleared of its protective forest by lumbering and grazing, less than an inch of rain brought mud and rocks hurtling down on roads and buildings below. The rounded hills of the Appalachians are remnants of a chain of lofty mountains far older than the upstart Sierras, as the Arbuckles in Oklahoma are the mere snags of ancient majesty. In the same way, might it not be possible that the great continental glaciers impounding as they did enormous volumes of water from the oceans contained the seeds of their own dissolution?

Here again we are handicapped by our ignorance of the play of solar energy before, during, and after a glacial period. But we do know this: with the lowering of sea level by evaporation the ratio of land to sea increased. Air moving over land and ice draws up what moisture it can, but in amounts far less than it could get from corresponding areas of ocean. As it circulates over the continents it has less to contribute as rain, serving in fact as a dryer. This we know to be true of the desert region of Baja California, which lies between the Gulf of California and the Pacific Ocean yet receives its chief masses of air from the dry Southwest. We

Nancy Bechtel

Deserts are not always hot. Snow in Arizona.

know too, that ice will yield to dry air even in temperatures below freezing, as sleet and snow vanish on very cold days in Nebraska even now.

If we include everything, great and small, that has been called desert we would be obliged to say that deserts, like mineral ores, are where you find them, without much rhyme or reason. But if we look hard at a world map showing only the great deserts due to climate and omitting the odds and ends due to local conditions, a pattern begins to emerge. True, this pattern is distorted by the irregular shapes and differences in size and location of the great land masses. But allowing for that, the great deserts of the world—Eurasian, African, Australian, and American, North and South—tend to occur toward the west and toward the equator on each of the continents.

This does not place them in the deep interior, far as possible from the great reservoirs of water, the seas that provide rain. Indeed the western margins of most lie close to the ocean, which is unable, thanks to atmospheric circulation and "rain-shadows" caused by the overgrown upstart mountains of recent geological time, to share its moisture with them.

Lest this reminder of the relentless compulsions of the natural world seem naïve, we might ponder the innocence of a great and good lady visiting a government installation which had wisely been put in an uninhabitable spot. Looking around in astonishment she said, "Why this is a desert. You must plant some trees and change it."

This queenly injunction sprang from a deep concern for human welfare. But mankind has had its career in a world of ice and fire—glacier and desert—a time of stress for both life and its environment. Never before in the history of our planet has the reproductive urge, compounded with such a powerful instrument as culture, enabled a single species to dominate it and press upon every available space for living. Not even the deserts of the world are exempt. In simpler times they supported handfuls of wandering people, living precariously. Today they are being invaded by a high technology. In the desert, as in crowded urban centers and the farm lands that sustain them, compassion alone is not enough to solve growing and insistent problems. Neither is the logic of scientific knowledge, however deeply it may penetrate the "secrets" of nature and reduce them to order within the human mind. To both compassion and precise knowledge must be added our store of historical experience, however imperfect our records. The deserts cover over a fifth of the earth's surface. It remains to be seen whether modern man will transform the deserts of the world. And to what end.

chapter nine

Too Cold for Trees

NOT all of the world's great open landscapes exist because of a lack of water. In the far north the limit of tree growth is set by long dark winters, short summers of long daylight, and permanently frozen subsoil. There is water but it is mostly frozen, and thus unavailable. Only low-growing plants such as mosses, lichens, grasses, sedges, and such woody plants as the heaths and tiny relatives of familiar trees—willows, birch—are able to take advantage of these austere conditions. Along with these are plants whose rosettes of leaves hug the ground in dandelion fashion. These bear conspicuous often highly colored flowers during the brief growing season. They—or their close relative—are well known to those lucky enough to be familiar with the alpine meadows of the Rockies.

Since the greatest expanse of these bleak treeless plains is in northern Eurasia it is not unseemly that they are known by the word *tundra* which the Russians borrowed from the Finnish. The Russian language has also provided us with the term *taiga* for the open, stunted forest that represents the northern limit of tree growth fringing the tundra.

A wide expanse of ocean separates the tip of South America from the ice of Antarctica. This, the farthest south of the great landmasses, extends only a little more than 50 degrees from the equator, roughly the distance of Labrador, Scotland, and Moscow to the north of that imaginary but significant line. Therefore little land is available for tundra in the Southern Hemisphere in contrast to the North. There are treeless areas in Patagonia to be sure, but these are grassland.

There are, however, good specimens of tundra far below the Arctic Circle, above treeline in mountain country and at progressively higher levels as one moves south. Without the perspective of geological history we would be obliged to assume that the plants and animals of these severe environments had somehow leaped or been transported from mountain top to mountain top, across wide and genial lowlands.

This fantasy we can discard. There is ample evidence that the vast continental glaciers ground their inexorable way south slowly enough to permit the movement of an advance guard of living communities, tundra replacing taiga, as the latter supplanted more luxuriant forests, zoned according to their temperature requirements. In North America, where mountain ranges run north and south, the way of retreat was relatively open. In Europe it was barred by the Alps and Pyrenees. Here many kinds of trees that had been common to both continents, such as the hickories and gums that require warmth, perished at the barrier like soldiers charging a stone wall. But in slow motion, of course. This accounts for the much richer flora of broad-leaved trees in the United States than in Europe.

Another consequence of the great glaciations was to chill still further the cool mountain tops, forming alpine glaciers and lowering the belts of vegetation until, presumably, the way was open to the tundra communities which had been driven ahead of the great masses of land ice. With the subsequent warming of climate that caused the glaciers to shrink, the successive zones of plant and animal life found their way back up the mountainsides, now preceded by the treeless belts of tundra. Eventually these were cut off by the forest that followed in their wake, leaving them stranded as lofty, isolated relicts above the timberline.

Today in the southern Rocky Mountain region the lowest valley lands are arid, host to such desert plants as creosote bush and cactus, with saltbush in alkaline spots. Semiarid grasslands ring these communities at

Saguaro or giant cactus near Tucson, Arizona.

slightly higher levels, giving way at the upper margin to picturesque open woodland of oak, juniper, or piñon pine. Ascending from this zone of dwarf forest, one encounters taller trees, first the rugged ponderosa pine with its golden-purple bark, then the dark and denser forests of fir and spruce which thrive up to the limit of tree growth. Above this are the relicts of tundra.

As if for our information, a record has been left in the sediments of the lakes, now dead or dying, that occupied many basins in the Southwest during times of more generous water supply. Characteristic plants of the several zones we have named produce abundant dry and dusty pollen, spread by the wind. Much of it falls into nearby water and settles to the bottom. These tiny cells reveal their source by form and marking and under proper conditions are remarkably well preserved.

Retrieved by boring, identified and counted, they show that (taking the findings from one of these old lake beds) the surface layers contain mostly pollen from the present desert plants, the remainder being pine from the lower forest levels. Several feet down there are few traces of any pollen other than that of spruce, pine, and fir. In the absence of any more reasonable explanation, we conclude that in a climate colder than the present the forests now found at higher elevations flourished lower down and much nearer, if not within, what is now an arid basin left by a vanished lake.

This particular basin, lying west of Socorro, New Mexico, yields further evidence of past changes. Below its highest beach line but well up on the slope, is a shallow cave, probably wave-cut. Within this cave is a heap of rubbish consisting largely of corncobs the size of a thumb, ancient prototype of the magnificent ten-inch ears that now yield a hundred bushels to the acre.

Radiocarbon dates indicate that this pile of corncobs was accumulated between three thousand and eighteen hundred years ago. Doubtless there was still a lake in existence, although the climate had become warmer and dryer by that time. It would be impossible today to grow corn in the area without irrigation. The Indians who grew it there were using what might be called "fossil water" remaining from more genial times. When this was gone they or their successors in the area moved to higher ground where springs furnished water. Around these springs are artifacts of more recent date, in the open foothill forest.

Some four or five thousand feet higher than this New Mexico basin, beyond timber line on the highest peaks, lie the isolated remnants of tundra that once formed a more or less continuous chain at lower levels. To the maize-growing Indians they were only useful, if at all, for hunting of small game or perhaps mountain sheep and goat. Dwellers in the great tundra plains of northern Asia and America have no choice but to depend upon game and—if near the coast or along rivers such as the Yukon—upon fish. Life at best is harsh and precarious.

During the long days of brief summer the surface ice melts into pools and low slow-growing vegetation revives. Great flocks of waterfowl and other migratory birds arrive. In northern Canada and Alaska herds of caribou follow the melting snow to graze, largely on a lichen known as reindeer moss. There are rodents too, notably rabbit and hare, and swarms of mosquitoes. The resulting economy has been geared almost completely to the use of animal products—flesh, fat, bone, sinew, and fur. In their use of these resources the Eskimo developed an ingenuity and dexterity seldom if ever surpassed by primitive cultures.

Their mode of life seems to have antedated the occupation of North America by man—an event variously placed at twenty to thirty thousand years ago. Our methods of dating the past are becoming more precise, but they are still imperfect. Somewhere between a hundred thousand and fifty thousand years ago, Stone Age man found refuge in southern Europe, along with bison, reindeer, and other animals that could thrive along the edges of the great ice mass. Their tools, and especially their magnificent cave paintings, portray a way of life remarkably like that of the modern dweller on the tundra.

Less handicapped by long winter darkness than the people of the Far North, they sought darkness deep in caves for their mysteries. Probably better supplied with food and other facilities, they found leisure to develop what is regarded as religious art, tied to the chase and to human fertility. The realism as well as the beauty of their paintings, done by torchlight with mineral pigments, places them among the great masterpieces of all time.

I once thought that their drawings, especially of running herds, were distorted. Later, a game commission on which I was serving ordered a winter census of deer taken from the air. Seen against the snow, the proportions of the running animals in our photographs were strikingly similar to those shown by the Paleolithic artist. He must have made his studies for later use from some high point.

Lacking the means and environment for art on the grand scale, the Eskimo has displayed his creative skill in his carvings on bone and ivory, while his legends that come to us are ample proof of his imagination. Today his ancient way of life is slowly dissolving from contact with an alien modern culture. To the Eskimo, for example, the organized slaughter of human beings which we dignify as war, is said to be incomprehensible. He will, of course, learn.

No better illustration of the precarious life of the frozen lands comes to mind than an account given me by a man who had crossed the path of the famous explorer, Vilhjalmur Stefansson. Stefansson was a hero to the Eskimo. He excelled them all as a hunter, I was told, but what really impressed them was his ability to eat food that even the dogs regarded with suspicion when hunger was the alternative. This may not be wholly fiction, for I met Stefansson once when he was living on a diet of nothing but fats. He had previously demonstrated that one could live in this country on an exclusive meat diet, provided he ate as much of the whole animal as he could manage. (Much that we discard in the way of glands and the like we buy back in processed form from the druggist, prescribed by our physician for relief of dietary deficiency.)

The survival of man and other animals in cold regions as elsewhere rests upon the effectiveness of green plants in providing food. Their ability to do so depends in turn upon an adequate supply of energy from the sun, carbon, water, and minerals. It also depends upon a range of temperature in which plants can live and function. Evolution has produced an impressive variety of plants, each with its own pattern of adaptation and many that survive under one extreme or the other.

In cold regions the long days of brief summer provide sunshine, while carbon dioxide, though forming a small fraction of the atmosphere, is well distributed throughout. In the oceans and other waters carbon dioxide is absorbed from the air, while the carbonates are moved by ocean circulation from the tropics, where they are abundant, toward the poles.

Mineral nutrients, like water, are in uneven supply the planet over. Where they are available they are used and recycled through the decay of plant and animal wastes for reuse. In the seas they must be present in the lighted upper layers to support food-producing plants. On land they come from and return to the soil.

Fortunately, the cold shallow waters that border arctic lands provide what is needed to encourage a rich supply of microscopic plant life during the growing season. This is the source of a food web that leads, step by step, to the larger animals of water and land—not only fish but the animals that feed upon them. Nor is the harvest confined to the sea itself,

Nancy Bechtel

Merging glaciers, Lituya Bay, Alaska.

for fish such as the salmon become available inland through their habit of swimming upstream to spawn. Here their dead bodies, left after spawning, help restore the mineral supply constantly being depleted by rivers which carry nutrients in solution to the sea.

Vitamins produced by the floating life of the sea are stored in the abundant fat of the arctic animals that depend upon it. Others are available in the bizarre (to us) form of stomach contents of the walrus, eaten with relish by the Eskimo. This salad, seasoned with gastric juice, consists largely of shellfish which in turn are gorged with tiny forms of marine life, including green plants. In addition to the other virtues of such an item of diet, the crushed shell fragments supply the calcium so necessary to the formation of bones and teeth. All told, there is little reason to doubt the reports of medical men that tooth decay among the Eskimo, with measles and smallpox, is a gift of civilization, a penalty of refined foods.

On land as in the sea nutrient materials are distributed by circulation, both vertical and horizontal and, save for the action of wind and water, by living organisms. Before the days of fences, guns, and plows the great herds that moved across prairie, steppe, and tundra carried in their bodies minerals derived from salt licks or pasture well supplied with these necessities. Their wastes and remains, left in the less fertile grazing grounds, helped equalize the mineral content of the soils over which they passed.

Thus on foot they performed an important role in the pageant of nature which, at great cost, we continue by means of mines and wheels. For a few hundred acres in fertile Iowa $10,000 was required in one year to purchase fertilizers and feed supplements containing fish meal and other nutrient additives needed to maintain production. The phosphates of Florida, which at some future time the sandy soils of that state are likely to require, are being scooped out and shipped away, while the fumes from the furnaces which concentrate them for use are now reported to have jeopardized the growing of vegetables. Only recently has any attempt been made to heal the ugly scars left by the strip-mining of this too scarce and essential mineral.

One of the amazing recurrences in arctic lands suggests the story of the Pied Piper of Hamlin, *sans* piper. This is the occasional suicide by drowning of the swarms of rodents known as lemmings. These mouse-like creatures, found in both hemispheres, have long been famous especially in northern Europe for ending a buildup of numbers by swim-

ming out to sea and perishing. In Alaska this happens much less frequently.

It is their habit to breed under the snow, living on the buried grass and
other vegetation. Like other arctic animals, for example the snowshoe
hare, their population fluctuates in fairly regular cycles. In North America they are the prey of fox, snowy owl, and a piratical, hawklike sea
bird known as the jaeger.

When the melting snow exposes great numbers of lemmings at the
crest of a population cycle, the predators close in for the feast. During
normal times the jaegers space their nests in the area according to good
standard avian territorial rule. But when food seems unlimited, they
behave like humans in a gold rush or oil boom, crowding their nests and
quarreling over booty often killed and only partially eaten. The result is
that fewer young birds are hatched, and of those which are, few reach
maturity. Thus the population of jaegers begins to drop in the presence
of plenty, indeed because of it.

A modern Aesop, with a shrewder gaze than is common among do-
gooders, would find here a parable for mankind and a rationale for the
old saying "When wealth accumulates, men decay."

Destruction by predators would, at first glance, seem to account for
the subsequent decline to a low in lemming numbers, but it has never
satisfied scientific curiosity nor explained why at times enough of these
animals survive for mass self-destruction. Quite recently an explanation
has been found, linking their population cycle intimately to the discussion
of mineral nutrients that preceded this seeming digression.

The layer of soil overlying permanently frozen ground and fit for the
anchorage and sustenance of plants during their brief growing season, is
thin and meagerly supplied with nutrient minerals. For a time these
minerals are used by plants and the small animals that eat them, until
the avaliable supply is locked up in organisms and their wastes instead
of the soil. As a result the soil, parsimonious at best, is able to support
only a decreasing plant cover. The lemmings depend upon vegetable food
and must either starve or move.

In northern Europe the result is mass migration in search of food.
The swarm moves over land, eating what it can find, swimming through
the shallow pools that abound in summer. And often, in its futile search
for food, on into the sea where no shore awaits it. In Alaska starvation
and predation serve more frequently to end the adventure. Enough survive, somehow, to continue the species.

Front of retreating glacier, Alaska.

Meanwhile the droppings and dead bodies begin to decompose, a slow process at low temperatures but one which gradually gives back to the thin soil the minerals needed for plant growth. Once more the food supply builds up and with it the lemmings begin their increase to a new population high and the drama repeats itself, as it has for time beyond our recording.

This pulsating up-and-down story of the lemmings has become more than a matter of scientific curiosity. Human population is now doubling in little more than a generation. For hundreds of thousands of years it increased slowly, always subject to controls not unlike those which apply to other organisms but relieved by man's ability to deploy himself throughout the habitable earth.

Such balance as existed was maintained by high birth rate, countering the impact of infant mortality, famine, disease, and slaughter in wars. How recently some of these checks have been softened is evident in the opinion of Dr. Philip Morrison. In his judgment, John Wesley (1703–1791) did more for public health in Britain by preaching that cleanliness is next to godliness than did all the physicians of his day. Modern medicine and sanitation are products of the past century as are the scientific agriculture and improved transportation that somewhat cushion the effects of hunger.

Everywhere today people are thronging from the land into great urban conglomerations faster than they can be assimilated into decent and rewarding lives. After prolonged and specious debate in which visionaries proclaimed the unlimited capacity of science to care for unlimited numbers it is now conceded that the population of human beings, like that of all other organisms, must be brought into some kind of balance with reality.

This is probably as difficult and involved a problem as mankind has ever had to face. It calls for a revolution in the values and behavior of an organism endowed with a powerful reproductive urge and the habit of unrestricted breeding. But it also calls for a more profound understanding of population dynamics than we have had. Today some of our best scientific effort is being devoted not only to the methods of controlling population by technical measures but to the broad study of populations of all kinds. Mathematics and physical science make clear that exponential increase cannot continue indefinitely. Biologists are now hoping to find innate factors that operate within animal populations to provide more humane checks than the relentless forces of environment.

chapter ten

Wetlands

L IKE an undulating and poorly drained pavement, the earth abounds
in shallow depressions, some continuously filled with water, others
only seasonally. Many are occupied by swamp forests, like the bayous of
the South. But many are treeless with a covering of grasses, sedges, reeds,
or rushes. Those with acid waters form enclaves of spongy sphagnum
moss, pitcher plant, cranberry, and low shrubs of the heath family with
musical Greek names such as Ledum, Andromeda, and Chamaedaphne.

Most of these marshes, swamps, and bogs are transient affairs, as the
geologist reckons time. Often they represent the dying phase of a pond
or lake, for both are mortal, destined to fill slowly with silt and organic
detritus. They may have originated where great blocks of ice formed
kettles, surrounded by stuff left from the main body of a glacier in its
retreat, leaving a lake when the ice block finally melted. Or a sinuous
river on flat land may have cut off a sweeping curve as it changed its
meandering course, leaving it isolated and full of water.

Where limestone is present it may dissolve in places, leaving "sinks" that become ponds. On an even smaller scale are the shallow pits that dot the prairie upland and are called buffalo wallows. Beyond question these shaggy beasts were given to rolling in mud, providing themselves with a cake that gave some protection against insects. One might call this a process of excavation by adhesion rather than digging. At any rate, it was effective.

Where the shores of large lakes and seas are bounded by neither rocky cliffs nor sandy beaches, there are areas of quiet water in coves and shallow bays. These too tend to fill and become hosts to marsh life. If they border on saltwater and are subject to tidal overflow they are particularly inhospitable to the growth of trees.

In contrast to the great reaches of grassland and desert that owe their character to climate, the wetlands discussed above are caused by local conditions. Yet in the aggregate they make up a significant part of the open landscape. In the Orient they are essential, along with their man-made twins, to an economy that rests on the production of rice. They are also, as we know to our sorrow, formidable obstacles to military action. They are exceedingly important to the survival of migratory wildfowl. Along the coast they serve as spawning ground for food and game fish. And wherever they occur they harbor organisms of scientific and aesthetic interest.

Inland the wetlands often serve as visible evidence of the height of the underground water table, as well as a safeguard against floods in time of heavy rainfall. Yet because they are shallow and easily filled and often available at a low price, they are tempting sources of quick profit for real estate development.

Florida, among its other attractions, is the tip of a wedge into the subtropical. It represents the southern apex of a great triangle whose base is a line drawn from Chicago to New York. In effect, it is the receiving end of a funnel that carries thousands down from the cold and crowded North. So far has this migration gone that formerly beautiful shore lines are being pushed farther and farther out from the buildings which once fronted them, hidden from them by new rows of structure. Save for remnants such as Corkscrew Swamp which is preserved by the National Audubon Society, the great cypress forest which I saw in 1918 has been lumbered off. The grassy Everglades, refuge for the Seminoles and safety valve for the water supply, have been messed up for agriculture to the point where elaborate counter-measures are being planned. Drainage has dried out the organic deposits, making them vulnerable to fire which could burn down to the underlying sand or coral rock. Drying and fire also make life precarious or impossible for many forms of wildlife.

Fifty years ago I was stationed at Dorr Field near Arcadia, Florida. Some thirty miles to the west is the Gulf of Mexico, toward the east the last of the lakes that abound farther north. Glade, prairie, hammock, and pine woods stretched away to the south and southeast, in a mixture that seemed at first to make no sense. The whole area was so flat that the usual features of topography and exposure that help unravel puzzles of distribution weren't there. Even from the air, so often a vantage point for resolving problems that baffle when seen too close at hand, the terrain below resembled a crazy-quilt of greens and grays. Exploration on foot turned up an interesting array of plants and animals. Quail and rabbit were everywhere. Snakes, including rattlers, moccasins, and coral snakes were numerous. One needed protection from the sharp marginal teeth of scrub palmetto and the saw-grass which covered much of the Everglades proper. There were hawks, buzzards, and the Everglades kite that fed upon snails that have become scarcer with drainage. Waterfowl abounded and wild turkey were nearby. One afternoon I stumbled onto a small convention of long-legged birds with the merest tinge of pale pink that identified them as flamingoes.

At that time the skinny Florida cattle were practically a form of wildlife. Today Florida is near the top of the list of cattle-producing states. One Florida day long ago, the horse I was riding snorted and jumped. Before us was a Zebu, or Brahma bull. He was as surprised as we were. It seemed to me that this chap belonged in a picture book or the circus, until I learned that these animals, with their progeny now so common throughout the South, had been brought to Florida by a matron who had retired from society and established a ranch. Anxious to build up the local economy, she had learned that the Brahmas were better fitted to the heat and insects than ordinary cattle.

The point is that the area contained enough natural pasture land to support a cattle industry, although qualified by climate and wetness to be forested throughout. The airfield was located on a treeless space called the Kissimmee Prairie—a mixture of grassy spots and scrub palmetto. No trees had to be cut to clear it, while the scrub could be scalped off with mattocks where necessary. The combination of open land and year-round flying made the spot seem an ideal choice.

From time to time we heard talk of a rainy season to come, but were never able to get very definite information, estimates of its arrival ranging over a period of several months. Then one morning we awoke to find ourselves in a shallow lake, the field flooded and planes to the value of a million dollars (then a very large sum) with wet bellies. The water was deepest precisely where smooth grassy turf, with no scrub, had offered the most tempting promise. The pine flatwoods not far away, which had appeared to be on the same level as everything else, remained high and dry.

Eventually it became clear, from ground and air, that the pattern of vegetation was related to differences in ground level so slight that they escaped notice during dry seasons. But given surface water enough, a picture developed as clearly as if brought out by chemicals on film in the dark room. Very simply, grass had no competition on areas that were regularly flooded during the rainy season. Where flooding was briefer and less frequent, scrub palmetto dominated, extending into the slightly higher pine woods above high water mark.

Off to south and east at levels below the prairies stretched the wet marshes known as Everglades, dotted with hammocks of cabbage palm and live oak and giving way further on to the Big Cypress, since converted into porch floors and spending money.

After nearly fifty years I am not certain as to how great a catastrophe, in terms of man-hours and property lost, the 1918 flood of Dorr Field actually was. In time of war any setback can be serious. What remains vivid, along with the logic of an intricate vegetation pattern which seemed at first to make no sense, is the fact that the field was located through engineering and political judgment that took no account of natural history. In that respect the experience was typical of what has happened and is still happening in many parts of the United States.

Explorers found and surveyors recorded many grassy intervales along the rivers of the Midwest. Some were puzzled to explain these variants on the usual forest cover. They were not in any way akin to the remnants of true prairie, nor were they submerged most of the time to warn, as do swamps, of the hazard of building upon them. But their very presence, like that of the grassy areas in Florida, was evidence that they had been flooded in the past and that the place they occupy would be flooded in the future.

Scouts and settlers of an early day may not always have been successful in trying to judge the promise and danger of their surroundings, but

Spruce bordered lake in Muskeg, Alaska.

they knew and respected the power of water and were familiar with the habits of rivers. Their homes invariably were on high ground, well above the danger of flood.

The men who built watermills along the eastern seaboard put them down in the valley. Visiting the old mill towns today one needs only a slight knowledge of architecture to read their story—especially instructive in the wake of a serious flood. Seldom if ever is a pre-Civil War structure (other than the mills) to be found down in the valley. Homes, whether tenement or more pretentious owner-occupied, are on the floodplain to be sure, but all are likely to be of recent vintage. In some cases a community kept silence while a developer built housing and sold it to newcomers on land known to be flooded every few years.

Harder to understand are instances in which science is used to the utmost for some purposes but ignored in other respects vital to self-interest. During the New England flood of 1955 a firm which manufactured precision instruments suffered damage to its plant estimated in the millions. This concern had sought the best technical and scientific counsel it could get for plant design and quality control of its products, but had placed its factory where no geologist or other natural scientist would have advised. In fact, this advice would probably have been available at no charge. It might even have been had from someone gifted merely with common sense and local experience.

There is no better guide to the best potential land use than natural vegetation, properly interpreted. But even in the brief lifetime of the United States it has become difficult in many cases to reconstruct the scenes that met the first white settlers. Most of them were too grimly occupied with staying alive and gaining a foothold to leave much of a record. Those who did write saw little point in writing down what seemed commonplace to them, while few had the training to understand what they saw.

Records once made have been lost, as were the surveys made in 1805 of a prairie in northern Ohio which I recently had occasion to study. Or they may require "special handling." A distinguished scientist retained to study a boundary dispute between Arkansas and a neighbor state remarked that the oldest maps were of little use to him. They showed lakes where none exist. It seems that government surveyors were allowed extra pay (double as I recall) for surveying water instead of land. Ergo, these gentlemen found it convenient and profitable to invent lakes and survey them.

Some fifteen years after hearing this explanation I rode across Arkansas after heavy rains. Our train crawled long distances on a track barely above the surface of considerable sheets of water. The flooded plains looked like broad year-round lakes, mute testimony to exonerate the civil engineers who first mapped the state of Arkansas.

Man has come full cycle in his attitude towards water. Settlers in the Midwest encountered many swamps, marshes, and ponds. Like the forest, these were rivals for space that could be used to grow crops and live-stock. They also produced mosquitoes in enormous quantities. Malaria, known then as "chills and fever," was a familiar ailment far north of its present range. Decades were to pass before the role of the mosquito in carrying this disease was understood, but this insect was so undesirable for other reasons as to justify draining its breeding grounds had there been no other excuse. Often muck soils, as those produced by draining swamps and bogs, were especially valuable for the growing of such special truck crops as celery, onions, and peppermint.

But wetlands perform a valuable function in holding excess water and permitting it to soak in. Often the more highly organic muck soil would catch fire and burn for months. Some would break down to a black powder to be caught up in swirling wind currents or "muck-blows." Fairly extensive drainage projects, especially in the north central states, turned out to be disappointing in terms of expected benefits. The loss in crops of muskrat fur and migratory wildfowl was not always counterbalanced by profit in production of tilled crops. And the red-winged blackbird, previously known as a creature of swamp and marsh, has behaved in a most unorthodox fashion. Instead of politely vanishing as its customary home was done away with it is now nesting in soy bean fields and it has turned its attention from waving reaches of rush and reed to not dis-similar fields of ripening grain. Particularly given to tearing open the tender tips of green corn, the red-wing now ranks as a major pest. Usually we are indebted to foreign lands (as they are to us) for destructive imports. In exchange for cactus, rabbit, root-louse, and potato bug we have received house sparrow, starling, codling moth, rats, and weeds. But the versatility of the red-wing is proof that we can grow our own trouble-makers—always provided that we upset the old balance sufficiently.

While farmers were planting strings of tile or constructing open ditches, other events were shaping to hasten water on its way. The network of roads, each a ridge between two ditches, was replacing the ancient meandering pattern of rills and brooks. Forests were being cut away, their sites being plowed as was the prairie. The old absorbent layer of organic material soon vanished. Horses, whose wastes were returned to the soil, come to be replaced by engines discharging gaseous material. Worse still, these engines make possible the use of heavy machinery that compacts the soil, making it less hospitable to water that might have soaked in for storage and future use.

The cumulative effect of these changes struck during the prolonged drought of the 1930's and again more recently. The modern farmer, like his city cousin, requires increasing amounts of water. He needs it not only for the growing of crops but for the use of his family and livestock. Drought damages his crops and dries his well. If he is lucky he may be able to purchase water from a municipality, but this takes cash, seldom in ample supply on the average farm. As an alternative he may construct a pond. Properly engineered and maintained, this will furnish water for livestock, fire protection (with lower insurance rates), fish, and swimming. Today such ponds are visible from the air by the thousands. Backed up by proper land management to increase organic material and loosen the soil, farm ponds probably increase the storage of ground water and help to restore the level of water in depleted wells.

While the individual farmer has been doing this about-face in his handling of water, public agencies, responding to a variety of pressures and drawing on a variety of reasons, have been constructing reservoirs and lakes. As with all human enterprises, benefits have been mixed; one may question the flooding of rich valley land to supply water elsewhere. Sportsmen and nature lovers do not always see eye to eye, but they join in warm approval of the purchase and restoration of drained, ruined marshes for the maintenance of wildlife.

In urban America, as town pump and private wells were being replaced by municipal systems to safeguard the health of populations growing at a compound interest rate, more and more distant sources of water supply were needed. Near at hand the disposal of solid wastes and search for new building sites became increasingly serious problems. Any marsh or swamp in the vicinity, under these circumstances, took on the look of a picnic table to a Yellowstone bear. To use it first as a dump and when filled as a building site seemed nothing less than an inspired solution. Where "sanitary land fill" was not a problem, taxes were. Any citizen who was enterprising enough to buy dirt and transform a swamp into a housing development that would pay tribute looked like a paragon of enlightened self-interest combined with philanthropy.

One swamp was situated on a hilltop facing Long Island Sound and separated from the shoreline by the railroad. The nearby communities were growing rapidly, so it seemed common sense to fill this worthless swamp with clay and cover it with new houses. Then came two rains, each of the intensity to be expected once in a century. The swamp which could have taken the surplus as it always had was gone. The water had no place to go but down, which it did, tearing out a stretch of arterial railway that took many days to repair at great cost to all concerned.

It would be interesting, if it were possible, to compare the profit realized by the developer of this storage basin that had previously served to balance water relations with the cost to a railroad already in financial straits and to its passengers. The health of a landscape, like that of a human being, depends on attention to the whole, not merely on dealing with local symptoms here and there as they turn up. We are ready enough to condemn the quack who pockets a fee for prescribing a pain-killer and does nothing more. But we are a long way from taking a similar view of the profiteer who tampers recklessly with the environment, charging the cost to future generations. It is time to apply the principles of accounting in the light of ecological knowledge. Too long we have depended on those who love nature to defend what is fundamentally a matter of our self-preservation.

Along the New England coast there were tidal flats or "meadows." These furnished nutritious hay and rushes for household use in Pilgrim times. They were among the major assets listed in seventeenth-century wills. As cities came to displace farming, these meadows have become dumping grounds, and later building sites. In one state more than four-fifths of them have been destroyed, the rest impaired by pesticides and other poisons. Osprey eggs have been rendered infertile by toxic substances that accumulate in the fish on which this bird depends.

Meanwhile the yield of coastal seafood has declined, in part at least because of the decrease in coastal wetlands which are essential in the early life history of animals that mature offshore. One does not have to be an esthete to prefer the pristine beauty of salt marsh to the ugliness that has replaced it. And whether one hunts with gun, glass, or camera, the loss of a rich source of bird life is no trivial matter.

Among the badly needed friends of wetlands, few have been more effective than the late Ding Darling. Through his powerful cartoons and his brief but glorious service as Chief of Wildlife in the Department of Interior he helped turn the tide of public interest and concern toward

Grassy Alaskan marsh with spruce in background.

this abused resource, as Gifford Pinchot had done for forests a generation earlier.

If area were the only consideration, the aggregate of wetlands would make them insignificant against the vast expanse of other types of open landscape—prairie, steppe, scrub, and desert. But they have been an integral, functional element in the total environment. And the burden of proof lies upon those who regard them as worthless.

chapter eleven

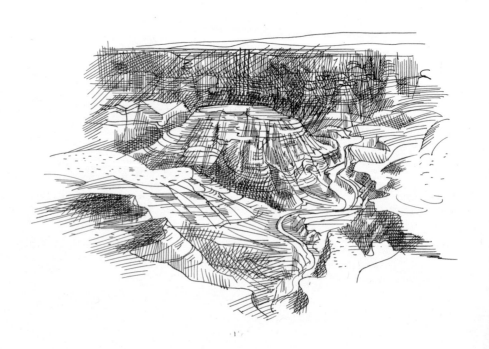

The Great Dispersal

THROUGHOUT the universe two forces operate to control movement and distribution—attraction and repulsion. Where man is the
movable entity we speak of inducement and pressure, exemplified, say,
in gold rush and persecution, in quest for the Fountain of Youth and
flight from starvation. As a rule in human affairs pressure starts movement, while inducement, real or imagined, governs its direction. They
operate in mixed proportions.

Written records began a mere five or six thousand years ago. Human
beings had spread over the entire habitable globe. Fable and tradition,
blended in epic poetry, tell us of the sons of Noah and their scattering,
of the wanderings of Aeneas and the peopling of the Pacific islands. But
most of the truly magnificent story of a million years of movement, of
trial and error, of promise and frustration, remains in a darkness that
continues to challenge us. Here and there a scholar, wielding the spade
and drawing upon the entire repertoire of scientific probability, gives us
an occasional glimpse of this great and unrecorded adventure. But for
the most part we must fall back on conjecture.

That the adventure had its beginnings in what we have called the Dark Continent seems now beyond question. We know most about its flowering in the north of that great land mass along the Nile. Out of the archeology of the Nile basin have come literally bushels of chipped stone artifacts. They are tangible evidence of long and patient occupation by men of the old Stone Age as they moved northward from their ancestral birthplace to funnel out over the earth through unforested landscape, ready passageway long before the art of navigation was developed.

There is no reason to doubt that our species has shown the same insistence on territory that prevails throughout the animal kingdom. Spacing is quite simply a matter of self-preservation. We need look no further than the experience of the United States and Canada with the Indians to know that several square miles of territory are needed to sustain each individual in a hunting or gathering economy. Even within such a group, however bound by kinship, the only choice is to deploy or starve. From these pressures within adjacent groups arise inevitable pressures between them. People, no less than bees, must swarm to survive, and often rival queens or kings must fight.

There were times, doubtless, when flight or voluntary emigration searched simply for "any port in a storm." More often, as Noah sent out the dove and Moses his spies, explorers reported the line of least resistance and greatest promise. To primitive people there could be no answer but open country so long as it was available. Such evidence as we have suggests that for them the forest was marginal, both literally and figuratively. As vertebrates came from the seas and man from the forest, both returned late in the game. Whale, seal, and dolphin are high forms of mammalian life; axe and saw come late in the history of environmental manipulation.

The great Eurasian landmass touches Africa in a region where forest is the exception rather than the rule. Essentially, even in times of greater moisture than the present, the roads lay open to those emerging from their earliest home. They lay open toward the northeast into the heartland of Asia and for a shorter distance into southern Europe. Eventually as men made their way into Siberia and learned to live in colder regions there came times when enough water was locked up in ice to lower sea levels and clear a path across to the western world.

Physically these early wanderers were a mixture of types whose remains foreshadow the characteristics of the groups we now call races. They had early learned the use of fire and for a time (guessed at as a hundred thousand years) knew how to fashion tools and weapons from stone. This they shaped by chipping. Grinding and polishing was a later skill.

The last great ice advance began about thirty thousand years ago, following a long interglacial whose open country was favorable to movement. It probably enabled men to move far to the north and there develop the skills now associated with the Eskimo. At any rate, when the last great ice advance crowded human beings into southern Europe they had boats and harpoons and other devices suitable to life along the cold ice front. Farther east, in Asia, there remained vast expanses free from ice, where man could get and keep his foothold on the edge of the Pacific.

Unless, as still seems doubtful, he had made an earlier crossing into the Americas, he was poised and ready to make it by the time that sea water was being drawn into the clouds to fall and congeal into the ice of the last continental glaciation. The time of his entry into the New World is not yet a matter of agreement, but has been pushed back steadily by finds of the last few decades so that a minimum date of twenty thousand years ago seems not unreasonable. What is agreed upon is that he brought with him fire and the dog, along with the art of chipping flint.

Man was not the first to make this crossing. Much earlier the elephant and camel of the Old World had moved into the New; as the horse, evolved in America, had migrated in the opposite direction. Here the horse remained after it had become extinct in its ancestral home. Bison too, as well as many kinds of plants, identical or closely related, span both sides of what is now the Bering Straits. Clearly these patterns argue for land bridges at times when sea level had been lowered by one or more of the three glacial periods that preceded the final and most recent one.

All that we know at this time suggests that human beings were not at hand to take advantage of these earlier pathways, as they did of the fourth and most recent. If they had boats, the pioneers need not have awaited the final stages of lowered sea level to cross. Should the earliest evidence of man in the Americas prove to be at least twenty thousand years old, the first of our kind to reverse the Columbian plan of going east by moving west must have done so two millennia before ice reached its greatest volume and sea its least.

At any rate, there was a long enough period favoring transit so that many may have used it. There could have been Adams and Eves in abundance to people a new garden, however un-Edenlike. Once across, they filtered southward until they reached the southern tip of South America. By what adventures they did this we can only guess since most of western Canada has been glaciated, while its Pacific coast, unlike the

Stumps of spruce overrun by advancing glacier, exposed on retreat, Alaska.

Atlantic shore, lacks a shallow continental shelf that could have been exposed for travel southward.

Thus the entry into the Americas was not their only problem. To consolidate their position men must have found times when there were breaks in the ice front that had formed by the merger of great glaciers from east and west. The alternative, none too inviting, would have been to trek southward over the ice, meanwhile finding enough subsistence to keep them alive. From what we know of the Greenland and other great expanses of ice, this would be a large order. Yet it is never safe to discount the courage and resourcefulness of human beings in the face of challenge. For the present, and perhaps for a long time to come, we must await more detailed information on the late glacial events in northwestern North America to reconstruct the ancient paths from Alaska into the interior of that continent.

One vital factor remained a tantalizing mystery until 1949. In that year the radiochemist Willard Libby reported a method of dating organic material as far back as forty thousand years. A small but apparently constant proportion of carbon in the atmospheric gas carbon dioxide is radioactive and in that form is built into the carbon compounds of plants and animals. This Carbon 14, formed from nitrogen in the upper atmosphere, breaks down at a fixed rate into ordinary Carbon 12. By separating and purifying the carbon in organic remains and determining the relative proportions of each of the forms of that element, the age of a specimen can be assigned within a reasonable degree of error.

The method was first tested against temple timbers and other objects of known antiquity. Once established as valid, it has been extended to materials from important sites all over the world, giving us for the first time a beautifully consistent calendar of events during the past thirty to forty thousand years.

Previous estimates of the final retreat of glaciers from North America and Europe had run as high as thirty thousand years and more. Yet with a rough knowledge of the rate at which sediments accumulate in depressions left by retreating ice it had seemed difficult to account for a lapse of more than ten or twelve thousand years in the Great Lakes region. Comparing notes with a colleague in Germany, I found that he had run into the same difficulty. The puzzle melted away when the exquisitely precise methods of modern physical science came to the rescue, supplanting crude approximations, and confirming the guesses of a briefer postglacial time than many had postulated.

Terraces of glacial Lake Bonneville, Utah.

For a thousand centuries of the glacial age, man in his various forms—a Pleistocene mammal—had been spreading over the earth and developing the arts of survival in its wide range of climates. No other organism save those fostered by him had so transcended the barriers of physical environment. Recent discoveries show that man harvested grasses in upper Egypt as early as 12,000 B.C. and probably cultivated root crops in Southeast Asia at a comparable time. Only in this latter fraction of his long existence has he been able to rise above the harsh existence of hunter and gatherer to domesticate plants and animals, build cities, preserve written records, and move on to his present estate.

Thanks to what Libby modestly calls his recreation from more serious work, we no longer need wonder why thirty thousand or more years of clear terrain and moderating postglacial climate had to elapse while men took no advantage of such favorable conditions to improve their lot. One-fourth of that time now neatly brackets their advance into civilization. By then they were ready for it in places as widely separated as southeastern Asia, the Near East, and Middle America.

Remarkable as the civilizations of Middle America and Peru were, those of the Near East and Orient far excelled them, and for good reason. The Old World had been settled for a much longer time than the New. The Christian invaders regarded the Aztec codices and other written materials as works of darkness and destroyed them with a thoroughness more pleasing to zealot than to scholar. We cannot share the thoughts of these people as we do those of Egyptians, Babylonians, and Chinese. We know that the Old Americans were impressive craftsmen, gardeners, builders, and calendar makers. They used the circle for spinning-discs and toys but did not have the wheel. Their domestic animals were limited to dog, llama, and perhaps turkey. The last of the indigenous horses had gone during the time of the early hunters.

As to their art—as to any art—there will always be differences of opinion. Much of it is overelaborate, grim, even savage to our eyes. Yet the geometric mosaics of Mitla and the carved stone effigy pipes of the Hopewell Mound Builders are superb by any standards. The jewels of Monte Alban, miraculously preserved from the melting pot of the royal mint, show a better appreciation of the proper use of gold than we who use it to meter wealth.

Yet what they did, and for all we know, what they thought and wrote, lacked the refinement and high organization that came to the older centers of high culture through a much longer period of incubation and interchange.

In this early and widespread dispersal of early Stone Age men through-out the Eurasian landmass, lies the fascination of trying to reconstruct the environment that made it possible. To attempt this, recalling that man is a product of the million-odd years of the Pleistocene or glacial period, we must resume our examination of the record, as revealed by successive deposits of the golden dust called pollen, shed by trees. Of these trees, spruce is notably significant, for it grows nearest the ice front. As the ice in its vacillating course alternated advance with retreat and readvance, so did the forests of spruce. We have seen how at the height of the last great glaciation men found refuge in what is now northern Spain and southern France, while many kinds of broad-leaved trees, driven against the mountains, vanished from Europe.

But a curious fact emerges as we bore deeper into lake deposits and explore them over a wider range of territory. In Italy and in then un-occupied North America, we find unquestioned evidence that spruce was preceded by lowgrowing plants of the genus *Artemisia*. This is the group known to us through the sagebrush of the northern Great Basin and to Europeans as the source of absinthe. It was abundant in parts of the Mediterranean area during the height of glaciation. Further east, as in Persia, it has a long and continuing history.

Named for Artemis, goddess of the wild, the genus *Artemisia* belongs to a numerous and vigorous family that arose late in evolutionary time and which still seems to be evolving. This is the family of composites which includes our sunflowers, asters, ironweeds and dandelion along with a host of others. *Artemisia* itself has some two hundred species. Since we must depend on its fossil pollen for any knowledge of its past and cannot at present distinguish between species on that basis, it would seem folly to draw too many inferences from its former wide extent during and preceding full glacial time.

Luckily the many species of *Artemisia* seemed to share, behind the diversity of detailed form that identifies them, certain qualities and limitations. Where conditions favor the growth of forest, they cannot compete, being shaded out. This any visitor to the Rocky Mountains can see for himself where aspen groves abut the sagebrush. By the same token, when dryness or browsing kill the aspen, the *Artemisia* promptly moves in. Again, the *Artemisias* of the world, when their locations are plotted on a map, appear to favor the dryer regions ranging from those of moderate temperatures into the arctic, but in general preferring cool conditions. If one examines the dossiers of the many species of *Artemisia* he will find that in the course of their evolution they have developed forms adapted to many niches, but always within the limits just described.

As a final but important attribute consistent with their other properties, these species are companions of another great and aggressive group, the grasses. With grasses, as with forests at the other extremes, the *Artemisias* exist in a state more or less of tension. When dryer phases of climate intervene, or where grazing or a plague of rodents occurs, the balance is thrown in favor of the sagebrush and its relatives. The converse is also true: given proper conditions, grass can replace its competitor, although often very slowly.

From these several attributes of a genus of plants not notable for its utility to man, we can draw reasonable conclusions as to the conditions before and even during the last great phase of the long age of ice. We can be sure that, despite the accordion-like compression and expansion of the zones of plant life during this time, there continued to be great areas where no forest existed to inhibit the growth of *Artemisia* and its companion grasses. Here, around the Mediterranean, and into the recesses of Asia, was landscape open to the migratory movement of human beings of modern type, members of our own species.

Unless, or more hopefully until, much more evidence in the way of dates, hearth fires, and assorted artifacts is at hand, there will continue to be a literature of guessing, educated and otherwise, as to the routes and sequences of early human diffusion. The most we can say with certainty is that the three great centers of agricultural origin had been occupied by the end of the last glaciation, America being the most recent. We know too, that open landscapes were pathways to these centers.

In each case the art of chipping stone into weapons and tools had been developed before men reached what were to be centers of settlement and agriculture. Fire, too, had been tamed and put to use, as nocturnal protection against hungry beasts among other services. Of these beasts, one, the wolf of Asia, is believed to have provided man with his comrade, the dog; but so far as we know not until near the end of his dependence upon chipped and flaked stone, just before he had learned to grind and polish his axes. This Neolithic, or New Stone, phase came at different times in different places and suggests some degree of settled life and leisure, as well as a new skill.

To what extent and when Stone Age men ventured out of, or were driven from, open land into forests is not known. There is good evidence that fire served to restrain the growth of forest at its margin, and ample proof that axes of polished stone were used in clearing. Denmark, for example, abounds in such axes of various sizes, but attempts of scientists to use them in felling trees were at first disappointing. Mounted on handles in the usual tight fashion, the axes broke on being driven against wood.

Curiously enough, a discovery due to fossil pollen led to successful experiments. Dr. Johs. Iversen, found a break in the record of a Danish forest, marked by the appearance of cereal pollen, gradually giving way to that of pasture grasses and weeds, followed by forest once more. This indicated an episode of primitive agriculture of a type still widely practiced. Called *milpa* in Latin America, *swidden* in the Orient, it consists of clearing by axe and fire, cultivation, pasture, and abandonment to forest. It was, on the basis of dating, the work of Neolithic farmers coming from the southeast, probably by virtue of a climate that expanded open landscape and favored somewhat open, less dank and dense, woodland.

Once more the stone axes were tested and soon the answer was found. By hafting them loosely, with enough play to cushion the shock and pass it on to the handle of resilient wood, trees could be felled in a surprisingly short time—less in fact than the haggling work of the typically dull hatchets so often used by poorly trained Boy Scouts or juvenile outlaws.

To complete the experiment the brush was burned by a rolling fire which spread the ashes without too much scorching of the leaf mold. One half the cleared area was left unburned and seed of primitive types of grain were planted throughout. On the burned area where mineral nutrients had been released in the ash, excellent growth followed. Elsewhere it was meager, suggesting that the makers of polished stone tools had learned to reenforce their efforts with fire.

As in modern agriculture of this type, production declined in a couple of years due to exhaustion of nutrients. Weeds and grasses invaded the area, which at last was being pastured, with woodland once more invading. For early farmers the routine would have been to move on and repeat the process elsewhere, exactly as the milpa farmers still do.

Actually this system of farming is not too bad, providing those who practice it do not become too numerous. When they do, not enough time elapses between successive clearings to permit the land to rest and the new growth of forest to restore its fertility. Trees, drawing mineral nutrients from the earth and returning them in falling leaves, tend to concentrate fertility in the vulnerable upper layers of soil. Here they soon become depleted unless managed with great skill, as the abandoned farms of New England and much of the area occupied by poor whites in the South testify.

However marginal the existence and position of those who entered the forest in early times, it gave them one advantage, that of defense. Whether they be the Picts and Scots who harassed the Romans in Britain, the legendary Robin Hoods, or the modern Viet Cong, forest dwellers have the odds against their pursuers. The solid fronts of warriors, so useful in open country in classic days and for centuries thereafter, found hard going against an enemy dispersed behind trees, as did Braddock's British troops in their encounter with the Indians at the Monongahela. For the change from phalanx to skirmish line those superb tacticians, the woodland Indians of eastern North America, deserve no small credit.

These Indians, far from primitive in their culture, were thinly settled. Their population in Ohio, for example, has been estimated at about fifteen thousand in forty thousand square miles. While they depended largely on hunting and fishing, maple sugar, nuts, and wild fruits, they also grew maize and other crops along river flood plains. Even so, they probably required the several square miles per capita they had. Their staple crops were not indigenous to forest country, but had been domesticated in their place of origin, far to the south, in the warmer, dryer, and more open landscape of what is now Middle America, nor did they have the means for extensive forest clearance.

There the maize requires and gets a long growing season. Yet somehow, in the course of many centuries of selection and adaptation, varieties had been developed and moved northward until some strains of this plant could be grown even in the short season of southern Canada. Lacking the powerful means of clearing away the forest which we possess, the woodland Indians of the eighteenth century and their agriculture remained marginal relative to the great food-growing civilizations of open country.

They had been preceded by the builders of impressive mounds and makers of beautiful carvings, obviously given leisure by a more productive way of life. Such evidence as we have suggests that these people were the first borrowers from high cultures to the south, gaining their foothold in the Ohio Valley during a dryer time than the present. Presumably they found the forest less of a handicap, dryer, more open, and more easily conquered by fire and tools of stone than it was in the later and moister time of their successors.

Whether we consider the massive migrations of man or the art of cultivation which has enabled his species to survive in great numbers, man, a creature spawned in ancient forests, could scarcely have reached his high estate except by virtue of treeless spaces.

chapter twelve

Settlement

WHEN one speaks glibly of the origins of agriculture, he thinks at once of wheat, maize, and rice and the centers of domestication of these three great cereals—the Near East, Middle America, and Southeast Asia.

But as we consult the pollen record—a window into the past for which we are indebted to the Swedish scientist Lennart von Post who opened it up in 1915—an even earlier indication of human activity is the pollen of two families of "weeds." These are the pigweeds, Amaranth and Chenopod, known also by various other common names. Both seem unlikely candidates for an honorable place as pioneers in the pageant of cultivated plants, for their seeds are hard and tiny. Yet they have the virtue of being edible and nutritious, while the young leaves of these plants make excellent greens. They are not woodland plants, but given bare and broken ground tend to enter and thrive vigorously even in dry climates. If any proof of their utility be needed, visit the dry bed of former Lake Chalco in Mexico. Here a pigweed called *quelite* is a staple crop.

Its young leaves are gathered as potherbs and its seeds are used as a cereal food. One may, in fact, purchase sugar-crusted slabs of *quelite* in village markets. These are not unlike our popcorn balls, except for shape. At the end of the growing season bundles of the dry stalks are loaded onto burros and delivered for various uses. Sometimes they are woven into paling fences. Even the woody roots can be pulled out and used as fuel. This weedy but usable plant is a meager substitute for the maize, beans, and peppers that fringed Lake Chalco before it was finally drained about 1900. Drainage had been begun by the Spaniards within a century of the conquest, after they had deforested the surrounding hills. Floods resulted. The engineer in charge understood the cause, but was ordered to empty the basins as a remedy.

The task proceeded slowly until the advent of steam shovels. The final effect was to convert a region of lush *chinampas* or lake margin gardens into a dusty expanse fit only for the growing of *quelite*.

Whatever the economic and esthetic merits of this change, its archeological significance is clear. It is a living demonstration of the value of a group of homely plants, worldwide in their distribution, to human beings living under very simple conditions. We have the record of their early association with man. Knowing as we do the aggressive habits of these plants and their preference for disturbed soil, we need no flight into science fiction to suggest how gardening must have begun around the dumps and pathways of primitive settlements. To expand these weedy patches and tend them would have required no utensils more elaborate than a pointed stick and the dawning knowledge that seeds, saved and scattered, would grow into mature plants. And since the pigweeds and their kin demand light to flourish, they and the culture to which they gave rise were indubitably creatures of the open landscape.

To the degree that these plants supplemented the wild provender from hunting and gathering, the amount of space needed for survival of human groups was decreased. More people could be sustained within a given space, the first requisite for some kind of community life.

Thanks to the rural people of Middle America we can make a shrewd guess as to the pattern, no less than the plants, of primitive gardens. Where there has been no change due to modern practices one may still see kitchen gardens, as distinct from fields where single crops are grown in tilled rows. Here the first impression is one of disorder, for the various kinds of plants are scattered and mixed in seeming confusion not unlike the haphazard distribution one sees in nature.

Yet this system, or lack of it, has its own peculiar efficiency, considering the absence of the modern scientific controls that make possible our present fantastic yields. Since individuals of the same species of plants and animals have identical requirements, they are potentially highly competitive. By scattering them among other forms with different demands upon the environment, such competition is lessened. Again, massed populations of the same species are a ready prey to epidemic due to disease-producing organisms or to devastation by predatory insects. It is even possible that in some cases adjacent forms of different kinds may have a stimulating rather than a competitive effect. For example, where blocks of trees in pure stands have been planted, those in the center are far less vigorous than the marginal ones that grow next to trees of a different kind. And there is reason to believe that a border of meadow around an orchard harbors fewer tree pests than a bordering forest. Conversely, there may be benefits from hedges around tilled fields, although these are usually discounted because the hedges do rob water from the nearest rows of crops.

At any rate, it seems safe to conclude that horticulture, the art of gardening, preceded the growing of single crops in large fields and gradually expanded into true agriculture along with increasing concentration of human beings. More food from less space and with less labor meant less wandering and more people in place. More people freed from hunting and gathering supplied more energy to expand cultivation and to develop a variety of skills.

Our own kind of man seems to have supplanted other human species sometime between 35,000 and 45,000 years ago. The earliest farming villages yet uncovered are in the Near East and date roughly to 10,000 years ago although there is evidence of still older harvest and tillage. (Chapter 11). Our predecessors had made use of fire and learned the shaping of stone tools at least 350,000 years ago. This leaves an almost incredibly long gap before the discovery of cultivation as a source of food.

Reasonable as it seems to credit the spontaneous growth of edible weeds with giving the hint that led to cultivation, the real revolution began with the taming of wild grasses. Of these, wheats have the honor of being in all likelihood the first to submit to human management. I have used the plural because there are, in fact, several species of this invaluable plant. Natives of the Near East, their remains are found in the earliest farming settlements yet uncovered. Barley, too, was domesticated early, as was millet in the Orient.

Grain and pasture grasses; a harmonious and efficient landscape created by man in Switzerland.

While wheat grains can be plucked, rubbed free from chaff, and eaten out of hand, as they were by the disciples on a sabbath day, they are most useful when ground into flour, mixed with water, and baked. By the time that wheat was put to use, men of the Neolithic or New Stone Age had become adept at grinding. Instead of the chipped stone implements that had been relied upon for hundreds of thousands of years they had learned to polish stone with stone. One of the valuable qualities of wheat is its ability to grow in dry climates (if its roots have enough water). But in such a climate stored grains tend to dry out and become hard. Quite probably, before the uses of flour were known, such dry seeds would be cracked between stones and moistened before eating. At any rate, the makers of smooth stone tools would need no intellectual revelation to devise simple hand mills such as those used even today in remote places.

Actually the mashing of wild seeds may have been a far more ancient practice. Although querns or hand mills are usually taken as evidence of the growing of cereal grains, Louis Leakey found the remains of one group of primitive men in Africa whose teeth were worn down in early life. These he considers vegetarians who mashed wild seeds many thousands of years ago and enjoyed a diet of grit mixed with their rations. In contrast, those teeth which he considers belonging to meat-eaters seem well preserved. I have found a primitive quern (*metate* and *mano*) in a cave on the island of Tiburón on the Gulf of California where it seems most improbable that the aborigines would be able to have anything but wild seeds.

Wheat has another remarkable quality, missing in its two great sister cereals rice and maize. Among its protein constitutents is the gum-like gluten. When yeast cells (which abound in nature, as the vintner knows) mix with sweetened dough, the result is alcoholic fermentation and the release of carbon dioxide bubbles. These bubbles become entrapped in thin films of gluten, causing the dough to rise. Leavened bread is the staff of life and one of mankind's favorite and most nourishing foods. In the hands of a skillful cook, wheat and its products are capable of almost infinite variety.

If we accept the idea that creative art is stimulated by the presence of a sensitive medium, we must admit that cookery, one of the great arts that distinguishes civilization, had the advantage of this stimulus in wheat, that most versatile of the great grains.

We believe that various species of men originated in Africa and that some of them now extinct had reached China and Java at least a third

One of the many uses of grass; thatching with rye straw, Denmark.

Women of the Sonjo tribe in Africa gardening with digging sticks.

of a million years ago. They must have passed through the great Near Eastern gateway, eventually to be followed by men of our own kind. Beyond this gateway to the Far East lay a great expanse of open landscape, never within human time blocked by forest. It was a tension zone between grassland and desert. In the great shifts of climate of this period, alternating between extremes of moisture and dryness, the proportions of these two great communities would shift back and forth. Like our own Southwest, the interior of Asia abounds in lake beds, either dry or saline, which once held fresh water. There must have been some intervals hospitable to wanderers, others much less so. Fortunately, this gateway was marked by the presence of great rivers whose flow was not dependent upon local rainfall, but came from distant sources, highlands where moisture was abundant. One of the rivers, of course, was the Nile, whose lower stretch lies in Egypt. In modern Iraq are the two rivers, Tigris and Euphrates, which join to flow into the Arabian Gulf and have given this region the name Mesopotamia, meaning "between the rivers." All three are flanked by the desert scrub of an arid climate, with areas of reedy marsh where swamps occur. Their two ancient capitals, Cairo and Baghdad, are about 750 miles apart, somewhat more than the beeline separating New York and Chicago.

Both river systems were cradles of early agriculture and the resulting civilization. Based on the excavation of village sites and on the natural home of the wheats, Iraq was probably the earlier. Domesticated first, quite reasonably on the hilly upland where it had been found, wheat descended into the valley as an irrigated crop when the art of controlling water was developed. By systems of canals and reservoirs which could be little bettered by modern engineers, water was drawn off when abundant and was distributed as needed.

The flooding of the lower Nile was—and is—seasonal and orderly so that arrangements can be made to anticipate it. Catch basins, extending up to high water level, retain the water to be distributed by a combination of gravity flow and ingenious and, until recently, laborious pumping. The twin rivers that sustained ancient empires of southwestern Asia are more violent and irregular than the Nile.

The legend of an ancient universal flood is repeated not only in the Hebrew literature but in other old writings of southwestern Asia. That it had a substantial basis has been confirmed by the finding of a layer of silt containing no products of human workmanship, but underlain and covered by those of the Sumerians, considered the oldest of civilized people. This sterile layer, seven feet in thickness and sandwiched in between rich cultural debris, is silent witness to a catastrophe. Understandably, this flood was thought to have covered the entire earth.

The strategy of harnessing the untamed Tigris and Euphrates had to differ from that employed on the Egyptian Nile. Canals were equally necessary but, as in our own West, they were fed by tapping the upper and higher regions of the streams. In contrast to the Nile, which gave its own leisurely warning, the twin rivers gave little or none. Only by careful respect for the calendar could their behavior be anticipated. And so astronomy, favored by the clear night air of the desert, was fostered for quite practical reasons, as it was later for use in navigation and exploration. Long after the Sumerians had been replaced by Semitic people, and a thousand years before the birth of Christ, the Chaldeans of lower Mesopotamia were proverbial for their knowledge of astronomy, but it is likely that the foundations of this science had been laid before their time.

With the Nile as a basis for reckoning, the Egyptians' need for technical knowledge was somewhat different. Both the Egyptians and their eastern neighbors had to be good hydraulic engineers, it is true; their skill in this respect has been confirmed by modern surveys. But in addition, the people of Egypt had to be concerned with the location of property limits following the annual bath of mud. Again, economic values must have stimulated mathematics and its application, surveying.

Both centers of early civilization concerned themselves with the glory of their rulers. If I read history aright, the Assyrian and Babylonian monarchs looked after this matter themselves with inscriptions boasting of their conquests, the mounds of skulls and heaps of severed ears and noses of their victims. The Egyptians seem to have responded rather to the pressures of overpopulation, by harnessing human bodies for forced labor on great monuments which, with their practice of embalming, testify to a preoccupation with some future existence.

Yet there were many workers beside those caught in the slavery of pyramid and temple building and that of the urban sweatshops where artificers toiled. Among the Egyptians there was considerable interest in the welfare of their own bodies, best served by the development of medical knowledge. Along with this, which ministered to their living bodies, there arose a good deal of practical chemistry useful in preserving their mortal remains and in such arts as brewing, metal working, and other manufacture.

How and when the art of growing cereals and the complex of vegetables, condiments, and fruits that developed around them diffused from the home of wheat and barley into Egypt is not clear. Neither are the details of its diffusion across the continent of Asia into what is now China. How agriculture could find its way across steppe and desert to become firmly established in new territory is a puzzle. Less so, however, when we recall that in historic time a handful of smuggled seeds or a bundle of cuttings has served to transplant important segments of plant industry.

There is, of course, another possible explanation. We know that in New Mexico the now-empty lake bed known as the San Augustin Plains must have contained enough fresh water to permit the Indians of Bat Cave to grow maize as recently as twelve hundred years ago. This water had been accumulated during the pluvial period of the last glaciation more than ten thousand years ago. Across the vast expanse of arid land which separates Asia Minor from the Chinese Empire there are many similar lake beds, some dry, others like Utah's Great Salt Lake, holding only salt water left by evaporation. It could be that for many centuries after the end of the pluvial period enough fresh water remained in these lakes to permit at least simple farming on their margins. If so, this would have provided a chain—now gone—by which the growing of wheat and barley could have diffused gradually into the Far East, where millet was already a crop.

So far as I know, we do not yet have direct evidence for this suggestion. It should be preserved in the sediments of these lakes, available to our Russian colleagues who will certainly find it in time if it exists. Somehow the idea of a gradual, progressive shift along a vanished system of grain fields seems more inviting than to assume a leap of nearly three thousand miles. Through most of the Christian era, cultures of the East and West were fairly well sealed off from each other. Marco Polo was regarded by people of the fourteenth century as an accomplished liar. Gunpowder and printing by movable type were known to the Chinese long before they were used in the West. For thousands of years two great cultural centers sharing a common crop but differing in many fundamental respects were linked only by the precarious thread of caravan travel.

Because the loess plains of northern China where wheat is grown have been treeless since we have known them it is easy to assume that this is their natural condition. I recall the surprise of the great ecologist,

Henry Cowles, when a Chinese botanist studying with him at Chicago dug up evidence that eastern China had been a land of forests, a fact now well established. This is another reason to suspect that wheat, a crop of the open landscape, had seeped in by degrees from the West rather than being transported by a gigantic vault. Only as men had learned to clear the woods with axes, whether of polished stone or metal, could the region drained by the Yellow River become the bread basket that it is.

The Chinese did not blithely forget their debt to the age of polished stone. In the Chicago Museum of Natural History there is a superb collection of jade. Included in it are early replicas, in miniature, of the implements so laboriously fashioned and so essential to better living conditions at that stage of culture. From this beginning of the art of working jade there is an almost unbroken series leading on to the beautiful and imaginative creations of later times.

The teeth, skull-caps, and thighbones of an ancient type of man that have been found in Java are far more recent than the remains of early humanoids found in Africa. The evidence left by Java man, dating back some 200,000 to 300,000 years, is evidence that his kind had by that time journeyed on its hind legs through the vast arc that swings from northern Africa north then east and finally southeast into the tropical limits of Asia. But for millennia he, and those of more modern type who followed him, were hunters and gatherers of food.

The warm and humid region of southeastern Asia is a land of forest and swamp and the natural home of rice. Yet there is no reason to believe that the cultivation of rice was a spontaneous invention, completely unrelated to an older practice of agriculture. Although this water-loving grass thrives in treeless swamps, these swamps are in the midst of dense tropical forest. Until the means of felling trees were available it is most unlikely that farming settlements could be established. Such means, along with the art of cultivation, are believed to have been present in the originally wooded lands of China well before the growing of rice as a crop began in what is now the Rice Bowl, although root crops seem to have preceded it there.

So it is that while an agriculture based on the growing of rice has its own peculiar techniques, and southeastern Asia is the original home of that crop and the place of its domestication, this region is not an independent center, as Middle America seems to have been, for the discovery of cereal agriculture.

Rice terraces protected by forest near Baguio, Philippines.

Like all plant life rice requires mineral nutrients. In natural forests the limited supply of these is recycled by death and decay. But under the pressure of harvested crops such nutrients are rapidly exhausted. Only by regrowth of the adjacent forest can they be—slowly, it is true—reaccumulated. If the forest is then felled and burned, the soluble nutrients contained in its ashes will wash onto lower ground providing the renewed fertility needed by exhausted rice-land for fresh cultivation. As we have seen, this practice works well enough unless the pressure of population becomes too great. When it does, the cycle of forest regeneration becomes too short for the nutrient supply to be recouped. This difficulty, compounded by the attacks of disease and pests, the lack of artificial fertilizers and scientific controls, keeps the world's Rice Bowl, now expanded far beyond its original limits, from being an Eden of security and plenty.

Even if the soil could be given time to recuperate between periods of cropping there are other difficulties in the steamy tropics. Land that has been vacated does not immediately return to the original type of forest. Instead it may become covered with the dense impenetrable thicket of smaller woody growth and vines which we call jungle. Or, equally bad, it may be taken over by the giant elephant grass whose stout, close-spaced stems and tough, matted, woody roots are a far worse obstacle to cultivation than the Johnson grass of our southern states.

Despite the abundance of labor in the Orient the problem of food production is paramount. Among the many difficulties none is more serious than maintaining fertility. In places this is renewed by occasional falls of volcanic ash. Elsewhere it has become necessary to conserve every scrap of waste, including those of the human body. These, of course, contain parasitic organisms that produce debilitating disease. In the lower reaches of the great valleys of China, despite some renewal of nutrients brought down by the rivers and the scrupulous salvage of waste organic material, there remains a delicate and critical balance among human bodies, their parasites, and the yield of food by plant life. Improvement of this dismal situation through scientific medicine and agriculture is a major concern of the present Chinese government.

As in all overpopulated areas, animal proteins are at a premium, for nearly 90 percent of the food value from plants is lost in sustaining the animals that depend upon it. This obliges human beings, as a measure of forced economy, to step down in the scale of food priorities and depend largely upon the direct consumption of plant products. So doing, they have a diet in which carbohydrates are high in proportion to the body-building proteins. Although this imbalance is met in various ingenious ways such as the rotation of fish crops with rice and the use of invertebrate animals as food, it remains a major problem over most of the crowded Orient where more than a fourth of mankind lives.

Within this decade, the 1960's, two American foundations have established an institute near Manila for the study of rice culture. Here in a brief time highly qualified experts in various fields of science have made striking progress, but are still far from the solutions they desire. Ancient patterns of land tenure, credit, and lack of equipment persist to complicate the need for crop improvement, sustained fertility, and pest control.

chapter thirteen

The New World

THE Equator is an invisible line. It is, like many other constructs of the human imagination, an important one. Repeatedly during the past million years, the temperature zones that parallel it in most irregular fashion have been alternately compressed toward it and expanded away from it, like the folds of an accordion. Throughout these changes the tropics have nonetheless persisted as a sanctuary for their characteristic forms of life, rich in species. Yet within the tropics, as elsewhere, available moisture and its seasonal distribution are critical factors in determining the landscape and its cover. Desert, savanna, seasonal and evergreen forests mark the range from extremes of dryness to those of moisture.

Although we have good reason to believe that man originated south of the Equator, his most remarkable developments have taken place north of that line. Here for one thing, he has had a more ample and varied stage on which to operate. The ratio of land to sea is much higher in the northern than the southern hemisphere, both in continental breadth and poleward extension. Civilization, for all its demerits, is still a measure of man's advance. For the most part it has been a northern product. The late Ellsworth Huntington tried to show that it was largely a result of the stimulating effect of temperate (more properly intemperate) climate, invoking climatic changes to account for the rise and fall of civilized cultures.

The evidence has gone against him, although he rendered a great service by clearly stating his views. We too often forget that science owes a great deal to those who, though later proved in error, have at least been explicit. His greatest oversight, recognized late in life, was his failure to allow for the disastrous wear and tear on environment that comes from the combination of too dense a population, whose practices lowered the capacity of its environment to produce food. Quite naturally too, he shared with most of us a preference for his own brand of civilization.

It would be folly, however, to minimize the role of climatic patterns in the unfolding destiny of the human race. The great plant formations with their characteristic faunas are an expression of climate, and these largely controlled the pathways of early human migration, while each new climate encountered by man challenged his ingenuity in devising means of adjusting himself to it. Of these climates, those which supported forest in the northern hemisphere made special demands upon his equipment and became the outposts of his early centers of agriculture and resulting cultural progress.

One extremely important factor has been the spread of knowledge and practice by contact between cultures. During the time of the great migrations, each group that came to occupy a home territory developed its own way of life, its peculiar speech, values, and beliefs in relative, though never complete, isolation. This, of course, is a parallel—actually an extension—of the process by which the members of a single species of plant or animal, becoming cut off at the margins of its range, gradually differentiate into new species. In the organic world man alone has been able to accomplish this kind of adjustment without significant changes in bodily form, by simply changing his behavior.

Once this behavior and the sanctions that justify it become more or less distinctive, they combine two conflicting qualities—capacity for change and resistance to it—mixed in varying proportions. As in physical systems, innovation must work against inertia. Change may come about through invention to meet an altering environment. But man is a creative beast and despite arguments to the contrary, change is not always the product of economic need. Beethoven and the astronauts have demonstrated this.

Mexicans are justifiably proud of the remarkable artistic and technical accomplishments of the original native population of that country at a time when it was virtually isolated from high civilizations of the Old World. Many, perhaps most, thoughtful students believe these developments to have originated *in situ,* without information from anywhere else. Yet the large carved statue of a wrestler, dug up near Vera Cruz and now in the National Museum, would not seem incongruous in a collection of early Chinese art. The late Miguel Covarrubias, artist and astute collector, showed me the richly illustrated manuscript of his last book, a discussion of art forms of the whole Pacific area, east and west. If the similarities are sheer coincidence, they are many and striking, leaving the field open for continuing debate between the diffusionists and their critics.

Doubtless the Americas hold some answers. Whether these answers are ever uncovered remains to be seen. As compared with much of the Old World, thorough investigation of its archeology is much more recent, due both to lag in the preparation of specialists and the number of competent amateurs provided by an enthusiastic leisure class as in the Old World. I was told by an American, long a resident of Central America, that the efforts of the Carnegie Institution in revealing the remains of the Mayan civilization rendered a more valuable diplomatic service than much of our conventional effort in the field of foreign relations. Their suspension, he continued, was unfortunate, for nationalistic as well as scientific reasons.

Even the antiquity of man in the Americas remains moot. Dr. Leakey, whose persistent efforts have uncovered the evidence of early humanoids in Africa, is convinced that men have been in the Western Hemisphere far longer than many American scientists believe. I happened to be present when a bet was registered between Dr. Leakey and one of the most respected of our diggers. The payoff, as I recall, hinged on a date of about twenty thousand years ago, Dr. Leakey being confident that within the next fifteen years remains older than that figure would be found, and his colleague equally convinced, at least to the extent of risking a hundred dollars, that they would not.

Until the evidence turns up—if it ever does—there is much to ponder, especially for those who sit on the sidelines while others toil with pick and shovel. Until seagoing ships were devised, entry into the Western Hemisphere must have been across the Bering Straits when low sea level had exposed a land bridge.

So far as we know, seagoing ships were brought into use by the Phoenicians after 2000 B.C., probably between 1200 and 1300 B.C. Long before that time American Indians had been living in the southern tip of South America, along with game animals (including the horse), that are now extinct. Elsewhere, in Mexico and our Southwest, they were hunting the last of the American elephants, the grass-eating mammoth, as recently as 6000 B.C. and perhaps even after that. The first settlers in the Basin of Mexico were dependent upon the herbivorous fauna they found there. Hunting declined after 6000 B.C.; the gathering, perhaps growing, of seeds is indicated by the finding of simple grinding apparatus associated with remains of this period. By 3000 B.C. and for twenty-five hundred years thereafter the Archaic people of the Basin were gardening and living in small villages around the lakes in the Basin of Mexico. The plants they grew, including maize, now considered to have been native long before human advent, were not those of Old World agriculture. This, plus their remoteness from the sea coast and the probable late date of ocean commerce, argues strongly for the independent origin of plant domestication here.

About the same time there was a primitive type of agriculture, without maize or pottery, along the Peruvian coast. This coupled with the prevalence of root crops in early South American gardening has led to considerable discussion of the possibility of transpacific contacts. There is no question of the seafaring skill of the Polynesians or of their use of roots and underground stems, propagated by cuttings rather than seed. Since science rests, in the last analysis, upon experiment, this controversy led to the Kon Tiki venture, successful in crossing the Pacific on a very primitive raft-like craft. Mexico and Peru—two remarkable urban and agricultural civilizations, were found and destroyed by Spanish expeditions in the early sixteenth century.

The desert highlands of Peru receive water from the melting snows of the high Andes above them. By a skillfully designed system of reservoirs and canals the Incas impounded these waters when they descended, controlling, storing, and distributing them for irrigation. They also developed cities of precise and durable masonry and a system of highways that permitted ready communication throughout the empire. Native to this treeless land were hairy relatives of the camels—llama, alpaca, and vicuna—whose fibers, along with those of the cotton plant, made possible one of the world's most remarkable textile industries. Thanks to the dry climate, specimens of these textiles—exhibiting all of the fundamental processes of fabrication—have been recovered and preserved.

A political and economic system which insured land and subsistence to all was based on the cultivation of potatoes and, where climate permitted, maize and cotton as well as beans, tomatoes, and other plants. Artisans found their opportunities in the working of precious metals, as well as in the designing of superb fabrics. In short, here was a great and self-contained civilization. Aside from maize, now believed to have been introduced from the north, it seems to have been truly indigenous, highly original, and in no debt to the outside, let alone to the Old World. Yet there was some traffic, as the finding of vessels of unquestioned Peruvian design in Central America attests. When contact with Europe was established, gold was traded for destruction.

Artists as well as lovers of art differ among themselves on matters of aesthetic merit. The Indian Thunderbird has little appeal to the connoisseur of Greek elegance. Nevertheless the beauty and discipline manifest in objects surviving from vanished cultures do afford some measure of their achievements. Beauty and discipline can be recorded in intellectual accomplishments as well. On neither count can the Mayan heritage, extending in a series of ruins from Honduras to Yucatan, be written off.

Monte Albán, a hill covered with the remains of temples and an observatory, is in a basin whose slopes are white with limewash, suggesting the former presence of a high lake now drained by a small stream that has cut back into the basin. Here, by good fortune, a cache of jewels escaped the covetous invaders and is now on exhibit in nearby Oaxaca, delighting the eyes of visitors and commanding the respect of modern craftsmen. South of Oaxaca are the well-preserved ruins of Mitla, whose classic covering of mosaic should satisfy even the exacting Hellenist.

Enough has been deciphered of the Mayan inscriptions to show beyond dispute that these people had developed a calendar of greater accuracy than the Gregorian which was in use in Europe at the time America was discovered. To the best of our knowledge these accomplishments were based upon an agriculture that had its beginning about 2500 B.C., thus several millennia after the domestication of wheat and barley in the Near East. The great technical advances in mathematics, writing, and architecture centered around the beginning of the Christian era. Art reached its high point in the eighth century A.D. followed by decline and ultimate disintegration, although a few centers survived until after the Spanish conquest.

European invasion merely supplied the *coup de grâce* to a dying empire. Many phenomena, probably with justice, have been charged with ending it. Warfare certainly, disease probably. The fact that the Mayan culture was not one of the open, arid, or semiarid landscape is significant. It developed late and at a time of high techniques in areas which, thanks to adequate rainfall, sustained forest. Its only recourse was the system of clearing, burning, tillage, and abandonment. This, as we have noted, works well enough until population pressure becomes too great to permit the interval between clearings to be long enough for the land to recover its fertility.

As adequate nourishment and technical skill gave rise to monumental religious centers and a leisured priestly class, we can picture the girdle of milpa farms and gardens gradually widening about each ceremonial city. Declining fertility and territorial dispute would, under these conditions, be adequate to explain the ultimate disintegration of this great and impressive culture. Although the Mayan tongue is still spoken its writings and arts have been forgotten, while the descendants of the Mayans still survive by the precarious practice of clearing, farming, and shifting.

Mexico City stands on the site of the Nahua City of Tenochtitlan, which was surrounded by lakes at the time of the Spanish conquest in 1520. These lakes were bordered by flourishing gardens of maize, beans, peppers, and squash. The gardens in turn were built up of fertile volcanic lake mud and cut through by canals that afforded water for irrigation and passage for canoes. Here, along with water fowl, turkey, and dog, was a nutrient system that may explain the vitality and aggressiveness of the Aztecs, although a famous mural suggests that human sacrifice provided an additional source of proteins.

This is high and arid country. Though often referred to as the Valley of Mexico it is actually a basin surrounded by mountains and with several hills of respectable size rising from its floor. Rainfall is between twenty and twenty-five inches and the altitude of the city about 7,800 feet (2,440 meters). Below it are lake sediments that have been explored to a depth of more than two hundred feet, or some seventy meters. In

Stone grinder for grass seeds, Tiburón, Gulf of California.

Cross-section of prehistoric beam, showing tendency of dry years to occur in groups, alternating with moister years.

E. Schulman

these sediments are the remains of extinct mammoths, camels, horses, antelopes, and cats, indicating a grassland climate although a relatively moist one.

Some of these animals survived the coming of man at a time variously estimated, perhaps twenty thousand years ago. The first tools are found around the beach lines of an ancient lake at least 150 feet above the present valley floor and later, gradually improving artifacts at successively lower levels, marking the gradual shrinkage of the lakes. The lakes were fed by water from the surrounding mountains whose supply varied with the changing phases of climate.

Pollen identified as that of maize has been found deep in the sediments below Mexico City, long antedating the presence of human beings, let alone the existence of agriculture. Here, as in Iraq, was a combination useful, perhaps necessary, to the development of that art: a native plant with large edible dry fruits; no trees to be removed; and ample water from the highlands to serve for irrigation.

Just how and when men began to take advantage of these resources is not known. But there is every likelihood that a systematic investigation of the upper sediments will reveal the beginnings of gardening. They have already yielded a record of the hunting to extinction of the elephant. Mammoth bones with associated dart points are preserved around Tepexpan, lying under some five or six feet of sediment and dated at about 6000 B.C. Whether these animals survived long enough to be a major nuisance to early agriculture (or gardening) is an intriguing question, as it might provide a double motive for their extermination.

Through vicissitudes of flood, volcanic activity, and drought—all recorded in Nahua tradition—men continued their occupation of the basin, developing villages and ceremonial centers. As hunting gave way to agriculture, the lakes continued to provide fish, water fowl, and invertebrate food. For this as for irrigation, the lakes were indispensable. At one time, probably around 500 B.C., they reached a critical low level as the result of the long dry period that followed the waning of the glaciers far north and on the high volcanic peaks of Popocatepetl and Iztacihuatl. It then became necessary to shift to higher ground, an episode marked by the great pyramids of Teotihuacan some thirty kilometers north of Tenochtitlan. Later, with the moister climate that developed during the early Christian era, the water level rose some four meters, to the height observed by the Spaniards in 1520.

Floods of course were inevitable in a basin receiving its water from the surrounding highlands. At Tlatilolco in the northern part of Mexico City is a pyramid whose base is some thirty feet below the surface. Actually this pyramid is a series of shells built over the original form as successive deposits of mud continued to bury the structure.

Volcanic activity is attested not only by the tradition of an epoch of fire but more tangibly by layers of ash and the great lava flow known as the Pedregal. Below this thick layer of lava, excavation reveals graves, artifacts, and evidences of gardening. Whatever else it may have been life through the centuries has not been monotonous in the Basin of Mexico. For generations to come its rich store of buried evidence will challenge the digger intent on making up for the loss of the written documents destroyed with ferocious piety by conquerors.

The words of a bluff old Conquistador, written when he was weary of hearing lies, give us some notion of the final flowering of a culture that began millennia before with men who hunted the grazing herds in a vast grassy valley. Said Bernal Díaz:

> The next morning we arrived at the broad causeway [between Lakes Chalco and Xochimilco] and continued to Iztapalapa. When we saw so many cities and villages built both in the water and on dry land, and this straight, level causeway, we couldn't restrain our admiration. It was like the enchantments told about in the book of Amadis, because of the high towers, *cúes,* and other buildings, all of masonry, which rose from the water. Some of our soldiers asked if what we saw was not a dream. It is not to be wondered at that I write it down here in this way, for there is much to ponder over that I do not know how to describe, since we were seeing things that had never before been heard of, or seen, or even dreamed about.
>
> . . . then, when we entered Iztapalapa, the appearance of the palaces in which they quartered us! They were vast, and well made of cut stone, cedar, and other fragrant woods, with spacious rooms and patios that were wonderful to see, shaded with cotton awnings.
>
> After we had seen all this we went to the orchard and garden, and walked about. I never tired of looking at the variety of trees and noting the scent each of them had. The walks were lined with flowers, rose-bushes of the country, and fruit trees. There was a pond of fresh water, and it was something to see how great canoes were able to enter from the lake through an opening that had been made, so that it wasn't necessary to land.

All was well plastered and bright, with many kinds of stone with pictures on them that gave reason for thought. Many kinds of birds came to the pond, and I stood looking, thinking that never in the world would lands like these be discovered again, for at that time we had no knowledge of Peru.

Today all that was there then is in the ground, lost, with nothing left at all.

Yet before the Spaniards came, to be welcomed as the white gods of Aztec prophecy, the people of the fertile basin had entered into the tragic phase experienced by other great centers of historic agriculture, notably Mesopotamia and Rome. With an abundance of food, population grew and organization developed with its fostering arts. Inevitably the pressure upon the nutrient base increased, stimulating an expansion of territory and resulting in conflict with neighboring groups. It was this conflict, skillfully manipulated by Marina, the native mistress of Cortez, that gave the small band of Spaniards an advantage over the Aztecs of Tenochtitlan.

The ripples of cultural influence that radiate from well-nourished centers extend beyond the perimeter of military expansion. Maize-growing Mexico is one example. But the extent to which this cultural heritage moved by migration or by commerce and other contact cannot now be determined. Was there a reverse current, like an undertow, in the waves of human movement that had brought men southward the length of a great continent thousands of years before? Or had the Mound Builders who left their spectacular structures and beautiful artifacts in the upper Mississippi and Ohio basins gradually borrowed and adapted what they could use from higher cultures to the south? The same questions, still unanswered, can be asked concerning the Pueblo people of the Southwest.

Culture, no less than fighting men, makes its conquests. But not in complete independence from environment. Before Europeans began to take over the Americas the Mound Builders' way of life had been replaced by that of hunters and fishers with a more casual type of agriculture. The effects of a long period of relatively dry climate and open landscape were giving way to dense woodlands due to the great reversal in moisture supply that had also raised the level of the Mexican lakes some four meters. As forests of beech and maple replaced the dryer more open groves of oak-hickory and the prairies, life could well have become more difficult for farming men still in the age of polished stone without work animals or steel.

The piling of earth into mounds did not wholly vanish, persisting among the Creeks of the southern states. But mound-building did shrink back from the outposts and quality of its greatest glory, leaving another of the many puzzles that taunt us from the past. Were the Mound Builders conquered and driven out by others or did they, by a conquest of culture rather than force, adapt their own way of life to simpler forms that made survival possible in a changed environment?

The New World has yielded many secrets of prehistory. Many are still hidden from our eyes. Low sea level during two times of high glaciation (the Illinoian before thirty thousand years ago, and the Wisconsin that reached its climax about eighteen thousand years ago) laid bare a land bridge between Siberia and Alaska. Whether human beings came to North America during the first of these opportunities remains to be demonstrated. Their presence since the second is well established.

The landscapes at the place of crossing and inland from it were tree-less tundra, permitting easy passage. But ready travel southward, while not inconceivable, would have been extremely difficult during the time between twenty and perhaps thirteen thousand years ago when, according to such evidence as we have, a continuous barrier of glacial ice stretched across Canada. There is some reason to suspect that some migration from Asia to America, at least of those fitted for arctic conditions, took place before the earlier of these two dates; none as yet to prove any mass movement toward the south until the path through western Canada was open after about thirteen thousand years ago.

Accepting the latter probability and recalling that the transition from Neolithic hunter to farmer in southwestern Asia took place after that, there seems to have been ample time for the Indians of Middle America to have learned the art of cultivation without hints from elsewhere. Once this art was mastered it is not surprising that by the beginning of the Christian era Peru and Mexico had developed a stage of civilization comparable to that reached by the Near East two or three millennia earlier. Whether or not any ideas or practices filtered in by a straying galley, junk, or outrigger from overseas, the high American cultures were a native growth. Here, as in the Old World, they were nurtured on open landscapes, dry climates, rich soil, and available water for irrigation.

chapter fourteen

Fellow Creatures

THE only quadruped to accompany man into the New World was the dog. And except for the cameloids of the Andes man does not seem to have domesticated any of the mammals that abounded in the Americas.

The turkey—a woodland bird—was domesticated by the Mayans and Aztecs, who also kept cages of birds. A vase of plumbate ware from western Mexico which passed through my hands to a museum is an excellent likeness of the turkey. It is probable that ducks and geese were also raised in captivity. The mallard readily adapts himself to human company. I was once in the office-studio of the late Jay Darling (Ding) whose hobby was waterfowl. On the easel was a big sketch of a mallard drake ready to land. My host explained that he was having a little trouble getting it just right and handed me a crayon, with which I added a missing line. "That," I was promptly told, "is not a wild mallard. Don't you see, you have made it potbellied."

165

One of the advantages of domestication is the production of fat and tender flesh. The Spaniards are said to have become fond of the meat of a kind of Mexican dog with fat rump and loins that had been bred as food. In rural Mexico today one sees an occasional animal whose build hints at this ancestry, as well as others whose resemblance to the coyote suggests past mésalliances. Human nature being what it is, other animals of various sorts, captured young, were doubtless kept as pets until ready for the pot, but there is no evidence of a systematic animal industry outside of Inca territory. That art belongs to the Old World.

The ancestors of our modern breeds of sheep, goats, asses, horses, cattle, and swine lived in the Old World. All except the pig were grazing animals, denizens of the open landscape. Swine, whose digestive versatility has been compared to our own, derive from woodland grubbers and eaters of acorns and other mast, probably the wild boar of northern Europe and a hog native to China. As man's clearance and cultivation of forest lands came late, so did the domestication of swine.

The herding of reindeer for meat and milk in northern Europe developed in a climate unfavorable to agriculture. So too did the pursuit of the caribou in arctic America, part of a hunting economy that suggests how the Laplanders may have eased into their present way of life. Whether the herding of cattle (cows, goats, and sheep) preceded or followed farming as an independent way of life has been a matter of conjecture and debate. The account of Abraham, the herdsman whose descendants finally settled in the land of milk and honey, may have had some effect on public opinion. And certainly there have been pastoral nomads throughout a vast expanse of steppe and desert since time without record.

As older centers of plant domestication and village life are being uncovered they show evidence of the presence of domestic cattle. While this does not exclude other possibilities it does suggest that their systematic use began in these centers, expanding later into pastoralism in the wide ranges beyond, where crop-growing was not feasible. Stable settlement plus the presence of fodder and grain greatly simplifies the taming of grazing animals, especially during seasons when pasture is scarce. It also permits the use of adjacent pasture when it is available, leading directly to the art of herding. Once this is learned and population begins to press upon local resources, groups of herdsmen may spread out and take to moving their animals in response to seasonal changes, in Bedouin fashion. If this is what happened, purely pastoral life may have come about by the swarming of men and herds from settled centers. The adoption of agriculture by nomads would then be a return to former ways.

However reasonable the idea of village origin of herding may be, it is only an educated guess, entitled at best to a Scotch verdict of guilty but not proved. The domestication of plants and animals is a complex theme that allows for many variations.

In a valuable but neglected book *The Conquest of Culture,* the late M. D. C. Crawford has summed up some of the factors that made domestication and herding possible. The animals involved had been conditioned in the course of evolution to the herd habit, dominated by the fierce and powerful male. Even the dog, before he became attached to man, hunted in packs. His loss of that habit, however unique among domesticates, can easily be reversed as sheepmen have learned, often expensively. I once had more than a score of sheep killed by a dog pack on a farm a few miles from a sizeable town. The surviving sheep were in such panic that no one could approach them. Yet so strong is their herd instinct that within a week after a negligent herder was replaced by a competent one the sheep gathered around him whenever he approached their pasture.

While the inherent trait of herd dominance favored domestication, it also posed a serious problem—that of the dangerous male. This was met by what has sometimes been called the greatest of early biological inventions, later and until modern times used to render human slaves docile. By castration surplus males can be converted into easily managed animals to be used for work or fattened for food. Males reserved for breeding purposes are still potentially dangerous and must be handled with skill and caution, as any farm boy knows.

It is practically the standard inference that the domestication of plants and the art of growing them were, like basketmaking, weaving, and pottery, the work of women. The husbandry of animals, on the other hand, is guessed to be a male achievement. Certainly the business of droving and management of recalcitrant individuals called for strength and agility as well as freedom from domestic toil. But animals taken from the wild must first be conditioned. To succeed one must begin with captured young and tend them with care, a task for which women are especially suited. Among primitive people women have been known to actually suckle young animals, while the modern farm woman has more than once demonstrated her skill in the difficult task of weaning very young calves. In dairy regions where surplus calves are available a small farm with little capital can build a respectable beef herd if the operator is lucky enough to have a willing and patient wife.

Having animal products available without the strenuous business of hunting stimulates further developments. Among sedentary people, forage and grain must be stored to tide over unfavorable seasons. Pits must be dug, baskets or earthen receptacles fashioned, and structures beyond the bare necessity for human shelter erected. Farmers in the dryer parts of Middle America make ingenious use of a large cactus whose trunk produces branches well above the ground. By removing the inner branches, the outer vertical branches are formed into a thorny basket that will hold hay and fodder well protected against marauders.

Milk and hides challenge ingenuity in devising simple but effective chemical controls, fermentation and tanning. In principle the manufacture of butter, cheese, and leather are based on practices devised long before history was written. Leather not only served for the making of bottles and other containers, but added substantially to comfort in the manufacture of footwear and clothing. Horns and clay later fired into pottery provided containers for liquids. Just as irrigation stimulated new knowledge and skill, so did early animal industry.

Textile art, which began with the spinning and weaving of plant fibers, was considerably enhanced when hair and wool from domestic animals became available. Varieties of sheep were improved by selection to provide longer and more abundant fiber. Fine llama and alpaca hair also made possible interesting variations of pattern for the skillful users of cotton in the Andes. Even among the nomads, who lacked the facilities for weaving, felt made by pounding and pasting animal fibers provided the stuff for clothing and tents.

Eventually the scheme of using the muscle power of domestic animals to supplement that of human beings suggested itself. Anyone observing a youngster being dragged along by the lead rope of an impetuous cow must appreciate the possibilities of such an animal for draft purposes. The broad back and convenient height of an ox or donkey is an open invitation to transfer a burden from human shoulders. A hungry animal trespassing on the spot where human hand or foot was beating loose grain from straw would suggest a kind of simple power-thresher—one which, is still in use in remote places. The price of such service is enshrined in the scriptural injunction "Muzzle not the ox that treadeth out the corn."

Once the use of ox, ass, or dog in pulling was appreciated, sleds or poles—in the manner of the Indian *travois*—could be used as vehicles. The wheel came later, as an enlargement of the circular spinning whorl. Not surprisingly the wheel functioned best on fairly level open land such as that of the early Near Eastern centers of agriculture, Mesopotamia and Egypt. It does not appear there until after bronze was available for the wheelmakers' tools. The mountain-dwelling Peruvians, though possessing spinning discs as models and llamas as servitors, did not have the wheel. Here as in the environs of Tenochtitlan in the Basin of Mexico, topography was not especially favorable to wheeled transport and human labor was abundant. Even the old Spanish roads that remain in Mexico are narrow and better suited to beasts of burden than to wagons.

Efficient harness was also a problem, solved for slow moving oxen by the yoke. It is still in use in remote rural areas. The horse collar which enables the animal to exert maximum pull without danger of choking was a medieval invention. Bits, to insure adequate control by driver or rider, were first fashioned of metal during the Bronze Age. The manufacture of this alloy of tin and copper was first known in the eastern Mediterranean region around 2500 B.C.

The horse as we've said evolved on the Great Plains of North America, where one of the most complete sequences of fossil remains of that animal have been uncovered. These show a remarkable process of change that began some forty-five millions of years ago with a three- and four-toed animal the size of a small dog, but with teeth adapted to grazing even then. Recorded in the fossilized skeletons is a slow increase in body size and gradual transformation of the feet. An inner toe enlarged as its companions shrank, while the structure corresponding to our nail became the hoof, which, unless worn away too rapidly, could replace wear and tear by continuing growth. In contrast to many other herbivores, where the persistence of two toes has produced cloven feet, the horse and its relatives are fitted for rapid movement over hard ground, not only by the structure of its hooves but by a beautifully coordinated pattern of skeleton and musculature.

Long after man's encounter with the horse—whenever that occurred—it was to him simply a game animal to be hunted for food as were the other large grazers. Its flesh remains available in special shops in France and on the regular menu of at least one well known club in the United States. It is still used in the preparation of dog food, while a traditional use is the basis of an old rhyme:

Old horse, old horse
How came you here?
From Sacarap' to Portland Pier
I carted stone this many a year
Until worn out by sore abuse
They salted me down for sailors' use.

Before tractors replaced them on farms there were many local rendering plants that converted horse carcasses into fertilizer. Yet during the centuries there was developed a love for horses second only to man's attachment to the dog. To such individuals the use of horse meat savored almost of cannibalism while the esprit of cavalrymen died a hard death. Today the use of horses, like other once economic practices, is steadily becoming more recreational.

Domestication of the horse seems to have taken place among the nomadic herdsmen of interior Asia where this animal flourished after its disappearance from the American grasslands. Various causes, including epidemic, have been invoked to account for its disappearance in the western hemisphere. But evidence such as charred horse bones indicate that its extermination was coupled with that of other large Pleistocene mammals including the elephant and camel that were hunted down as recently as six or seven thousand years B.C. After the Spaniards reintroduced the horse to the western hemisphere, escaped horses quickly formed large herds perfectly adapted to life on the Great Plains. Remnants of these herds still survive in remote pockets, as do the pony descendants of shipwrecked horses on islands offshore from the Atlantic coast. On islands where space and food are limited small horses have a survival advantage over larger ones.

Elsewhere selection both by man and nature has produced many types of domestic horse. Precursors of the powerful modern draft horses, medieval chargers were bred to carry the knight with his heavy hardware to lend momentum to his leveled lance.

To the Bedouin, whose way of life puts a premium on swift movement, the advantage of selecting for speed is clear enough. The Arabian horse whose grace is an expression of function as well as beauty is his answer.

Once the art of horsemanship was developed it produced a new kind of symbiosis, illustrated in fables of the Centaur who combined human intelligence with equine swiftness, welded together in a single unit. The ease and range of the herdsman were vastly increased as was his mobility in raiding. Warfare took on new methods and new dimensions, placing foot soldiery at a disadvantage in many respects. Cavalry became the eyes of the army, able to make quick reconnaissance to locate enemy forces. Equipped with long lance, short powerful bow, and scimitar or sabre the cavalryman possessed both a physical and psychological advantage over unmounted troops. Even where spearmen in solid formation could repel a cavalry charge and were backed by archers on foot, such infantry could be flanked and routed by fast-moving horsemen.

In many respects the rapid cultural evolution of the Plains Indians suggests what must have happened several thousands of years earlier in the Old World. Whatever thievery and aggression they may have practiced before they had access to the horse, these practices quickly intensified thereafter. Like the wild Asiatics, the Plains Indians were not metal workers, but like them they found plenty of traders willing to supply them with arms and to purchase stolen animals. Thus equipped, encroachment by white troops and settlers gave the Indians ample reason for retaliation, while competition with other tribes for space stepped up the rate of internecine strife.

There were, however, differences that have left their stamp on history. The Indian was on the defensive against the advances of a more prosperous and technically powerful culture coming at him from east and south. He seems to have been more concerned to preserve his own way of life than to adopt that of his enemies which, aided by money, alcohol, and disease, easily corrupted him. The institution of private property in land was alien to him and deadly to his hunting habit.

The horsemen of the Asiatic steppes on the other hand offered little temptation to more advanced cultures. The geography of climate and vegetation placed them between the Chinese and Near-Eastern empires, each nourished by agriculture, each grown fat and rich with luxuries. Instead of being on the defensive they were relatively secure from external enemies. Such commerce as there was between China and the West was obliged to cross their territory. Traders at both margins were ready to barter with them. They were familiar with the gold and goods of more sedentary neighbors, and covetous of them.

Though wood was scarce the Mongols were able to shape deadly bows by splicing such materials as they had, especially bone and sinew, and to obtain other weaponry from merchants as eager to trade with them as our frontier peddlers of a later day were to supply the Indians with guns and whiskey in exchange for hides and horses. They were nourished by the meat and milk of their herds and kept vigorous by their way of life. Their neighbors on either side were softer in a military sense, in spite of their professional armies, while their visible wealth set them up as targets.

Added to such inducements were recurring internal pressures—their own growth in numbers, and the inevitable pattern of treeless climates where periods of drought intervene between those more favorable to the production of ample pastures. As we know from more recent experience, abundant moisture and vegetation encourage expansion of herds and increase of the numbers of people that can be sustained by them. As the range becomes overcrowded it is more closely grazed, giving it less opportunity to keep pace with consumption. Should severe and protracted drought come at such a time, escape is the only answer for the people caught in this disaster. Casual raids on exposed farm villages may thus be replaced by mass migration, the invasion and pillage by barbarian hordes so familiar in classic history, both of China and the Roman Empire.

Whether as raiding or as larger scale conquest, this pattern probably goes back long before it was recorded for our information. It is now (and reasonably) assumed by historians that the recurrence of drought was involved in the more massive group movements. Unless our scientific enterprise is totally diverted from the business of learning to understand to the business of trying to "conquer" our environment, we now have the means of knowing quite precisely the degree to which environmental change has interacted with cupidity in shaping the spectacular mass movements which have played so great and often tragic a role in human affairs. Witness the barbarian invasions of Italy and the Mongol conquests of China and India.

As in geology where the slow wearing down of rocks and accumulation of sediment leads in time to massive change, so lesser raiding on the eastern and western edges of the great arid interior of Eurasia has had its cumulative effects. Repeatedly groups of nomads, seizing agricultural territory, have settled and adopted a new way of life. So doing they have come to incur the disadvantages as well as the benefits of this change. In a few generations they become easy prey to those of their former habit, giving way to their own less domesticated kinsmen. By descent and on the tenuous grounds of high ethics, all men are brethren. But brotherly behavior remains a rare attainment, as it has always been. And involved in this long chronicle of discord in many ways, some obvious, some more subtle, has been man's intricate relationship to his fellow creatures.

Other animals besides cattle, sheep, horses, and swine have played important roles in the human drama, some in humble, others in destructive ways. We have mentioned the ambivalent services of the goat, source of meat and milk, yet a major factor in denuding the landscape. A complete liability has been the rat, dispenser of disease and, along with insects, man's great competitor for his food reserves. Plague, recurrent in the Orient and spread to man from rats by fleas, destroyed at least half of the population of Europe in the fourteenth century and brought disaster to Stuart England. Aside from the horrible suffering it caused, plague has had important economic and social effects by impoverishing the labor market. Some who interpret history in economic terms have seen in the loss of workers due to plague and wars a factor that helped bring about the Industrial Revolution. When labor is scarce, it stimulates the search for substitutes.

Two animals native to desert regions, camel and ass, have served man for millennia by carrying burdens which otherwise would have weighed on his own shoulders. The camel family, like the horses, originated in North America, spreading to Asia and South America, but surviving in its first home until after the arrival of man. By their ability to store reserve fat and water, camels of the Old World, their nostrils and feet adapted to desert sands, have made it possible for commerce to cross the great forbidding Gobi and Sahara wastes. Throughout history the camel has served as a link between cultures which, without it, would have been effectively isolated from each other.

The ass, with the zebra a surviving member of the once varied horse family, shares with the camel an ability to endure hot, dry conditions and to work with minimum upkeep. Tribute to these plodding servants may seem quaint to a generation accustomed to using the energy from fossil fuel. But now that civilization has the means of its own destruction, should man implement that power and any survive, it may be necessary to return to simpler ways and means.

The elephant, third member of the trio of burden-bearers, seems to have been first domesticated in Egypt. Like the others it is an eater of plants, well adapted to the mixture of woodland and grass we call savanna. It is amenable, especially in its Asiatic form, to the discipline of human handlers. By virtue of its muscular trunk it is a lifter as well as a carrier, while the ivory of its tusks has had a long history in the arts and commerce and by no means a minor role in the slave trade. Once used in war, this largest of land mammals still serves in hunting and ceremony as well as in the more practical field of tropical forestry.

Most of man's animal servitors are creatures of the open landscape, and vegetarians. Two companions that can make themselves useful when necessary, are carnivores—cat and dog. They share man's fondness for flesh. Through selection both cat and dog have developed many varieties. Traditionally the cat has been the best defense against predatory rodents. This benefaction, along with its sinuous grace, is enough to account for the esteem in which it was held by the Egyptians, storers of grain and lovers of beauty. The disdainful Siamese, whose discipline by us is usually limited to toilet training, was bred for hunting and retrieving. That cats can be trained was perfectly demonstrated to me in Honolulu where a tawny Tom daily took his place in the midst of feeding doves, cardinals, and other birds. On one occasion he attacked and drove off another of his kind who entered this peaceful scene in the hope of a free lunch.

The story of the dog and his versatile services to our species is so well known and so often told that it calls for little comment here. Its devotion has survived hunger, hardship, and often brutal treatment from the days when it became hunting companion and guardian of early man. Were it not for the dog that has accompanied him, man would be the only higher form of animal life that has transcended all the barriers of climate and condition to spread over the entire habitable globe.

chapter fifteen

Forest—Friend and Rival

IN a world as complex as ours it is inevitable that man, singly and in groups, should be of two minds, as we say, about many things. Among such things, the forest is a striking example. Man, forest-born, emerged from this cradle to spread over the earth, developing agriculture and cities largely by grace of landscapes that were open and unforested. As suitable tools were devised he began to fell trees to build his temples, houses, and ships. Even earlier, having learned to manipulate fire, he found the value of wood as fuel—a use which continues to the present.

Swarming out from the population centers made possible by the art of domestication, men found another advantage in the cutting down of trees. Not unlike the killing off or driving out of rival groups of human beings, destruction of the forest made space available to be used for growing of crops and grazing of livestock, as well as habitation. To this end fire not only sped up the labor of clearance, but, in a fashion mysterious until the rise of modern chemistry, insured at least a brief period of abundant crops. This benefit, as we know, was due to the release of potash and other mineral nutrients that had slowly accumulated in the wood.

Thus, from times remote beyond our records but in guessable fashion, our ancestors learned to value forests for their products, yet coveted the space required to yield fuel, building material, and other useful stuffs. With the ultimate development of a money economy and mass transportation, this ambivalence came into sharper focus. The nineteenth century, which saw a sobered Europe conserving its woodlands, witnessed an incredibly ruthless exploitation of the North American continent. So brazen and destructive was it that an energetic president and his counselors were able to arouse public concern and inaugurate the beginnings of a forestry policy soon after the end of the century.

Meanwhile considerable progress has been made, not only in setting aside public reserves, but in sustained yield practices by large corporations. These latter, now responsible to stockholders instead of single owners, have seen the necessity of insuring future supplies of raw material and are not inconsiderate of the value of public goodwill. Yet ambivalence still prevails within our western society. As I write, the magnificent remnants of coastal redwoods are the subject of a tug-of-war. One group, desiring to get through them as fast as possible, supports the cutting of straight highways. Others who wish to observe and enjoy these venerable trees at leisure do not favor this type of engineering efficiency. Again, a considerable body of public opinion urges government to acquire extensive holdings whose present owners resent this threat to future profits that are reckoned as legitimate under our system.

Scant knowledge of legend, poetry, and the fine arts is needed to show that the subject of trees touches depths in human nature far beyond simple profit and loss. We know that in Mexico trees were cut simply because some Spaniard was "homesick for the treeless plains of Castile." To some the quiet of the deep forest brings spiritual refreshment, to others gloom and depression. One man looks at an ancient tree with a calculating eye to the number of board feet, his neighbor with a feeling of aesthetic pleasure.

In two short generations we have emerged from the personal confrontations and relative simplicities of village and town life into a world of speed, noise, number, anonymity, and infinite complication. Mud roads, family horses, backyard wells, gardens and poultry, country stores, and all that went with this kind of existence have been swept away as the chain of custom that links the individual to his natural environment has become longer and more tenuous. Clarity of perception and thought, never too generously distributed among human beings, becomes steadily more difficult to achieve. Even the sciences with their promises of new certainty have not insured it.

Man's attitude to what a poet might call a superb evidence of Nature's generosity—the forest—has long been one of ambivalence. To the treeless regions of early agriculture and civilization, wood was an important article of commerce. This alone, in due time, would have led to extensive clearance of tributary mountainsides. Perhaps even more insistent was the need for fuel and, as flocks and herds increased, for pasturage.

Actually, the destruction of forests can go on without the felling of trees by cutting tools. Fire, whether set by lightning or human hands, is a powerful agent. But so are domestic animals. When Captain Cook and later George Vancouver visited the Hawaiian Islands in the late eighteenth century they released pairs of livestock to insure meat supplies for future explorers. As these animals multiplied they consumed the foliage within reach, particularly that of seedlings. They trampled the ground and as the old trees died there was no replacement. Within less than two centuries the lush native forest was reduced to remnants not easily accessible. Elsewhere the ground became as treeless as a shortgrass hill in Wyoming.

After the islands became an American possession and cities developed, the question of adequate water supply became critical. Reforestation was necessary to prevent excessive runoff. The simplest solution seemed to be to import fast-growing eucalyptus trees from Australia. Mostly these were species of little value as timber. The leaves and litter of these exotics contain chemicals which resist decay. In place of the rich humus of the native forest with its undergrowth of spongy moss and fern, the forest floor beneath the eucalypts is dry and sterile. If some way could be found (and it might not be easy) to restore the original vegetation it would be far more absorptive and at the same time yield valuable products, notably beautiful cabinet woods.

The forests of the Near East, including the famous cedars of Lebanon, exist today as small scattered islands on the mountainsides. Those which in 1500 surrounded the Basin of Mexico were virtually gone within a century of the Spanish conquest, due to the demand for charcoal, building material and in no small measure to the cattle introduced, in the words of a contemporary engineer, by *los cristianos*.

To these losses must be added those due to an almost world-wide practice of shifting agriculture. This kind of farming is largely confined to regions that are marginal for agriculture. As in ancient practice, blocks of trees are cut and burned, releasing the mineral nutrients in the wood. These, together with what nutrients are present in the thin layer of surface organic material, serve for a few years at most to nourish planted crops. When exhausted the field is abandoned and the process repeated.

In principle the forest may be expected to return and, given time, to build up a temporary fertility once more. Too often it happens that population grows, increasing the pressure for food so much that the recovery phase of the cycle is shortened. There is every reason to believe that the impressive cities of the Mayans in Central America were victims, at least in part, of this kind of soil depletion. Eventually they were obliged to clear and cultivate the land before the second growth had time to render it once more productive. This would eventually surround them with widening belts that could not produce the necessary crops. That erosion of this too frequently cleared surface must also have taken place is evident from the many lake basins now filled with silt and clay.

Another hazard develops in the warm, humid parts of Asia. Here the abandoned land is often taken over by the giant, deeply rooted, and intractable elephant grass. I have never seen this region, but the problem of reclaiming such land has been vividly described to me by Indonesians who have had to live with it. The dense growth of elephant grass is not only difficult to penetrate but almost impossible to clear and replace with cultivated crops.

The abundant moisture supply necessary for forest has some interesting consequences. Percolating through the soil it adds to the underground supply of springs and rivers. But it also tends to carry with it the more soluble nutrient salts of calcium and potassium. The tight packed leaf litter on the forest floor tends to ferment, being only partly oxidized. This results in forming organic acids which further encourage the dissolving of alkaline minerals from the soil layer directly below the humus material. As a consequence this layer, when exposed by clearing and cultivation, is likely to be poor in the material which crops need, although they thrive for a time on that which is contained in the leaf mold at the surface.

Again because surface and ground water are readily available in regions that are or have been forested, water supply is not usually a limiting factor for man. Rivers, lakes, and the ocean waters frequently nearby provide easy travel and, until contaminated by silt and human wastes, a generous supply of fish. Thus areas of climate suitable for the growth of trees are inviting to dense human populations, also fostered by the abundance of building material and fuel. Even the tropical rain forest, though otherwise unfavorable in many respects, can be supplanted by wet culture of rice to nourish large numbers of people.

Viewed in historical perspective the first great aggregations of human beings were in open landscapes of arid climate provided with the water of great rivers coming down from far-away wooded heights with abundant rainfall. It later became possible to invade the forested regions of the earth, open them up and create, as a secondary phenomenon, such centers of heavy population as Belgium, China, and New England.

The limitations of more humid climates (including flood) have been met in various ways. The Chinese have laboriously met the depletion of soil nutrients by patiently conserving all types of organic waste. It has been said, with considerable truth, that the balance among green plants that produce food, human beings who eat it, and the parasites of many kinds that live upon both, is like that of a spring under critical tension. Add to these factors flood and drought, all imposed upon high birth rate and crowded living, and nothing better can be expected than heavy infant mortality and short life span.

Early man seems to have colonized the earth mostly by travel over open, unforested landscapes and in them learned the art of cultivation. Savanna conditions prevailed in what is now the Egyptian desert during the late glacial period, 12000 B.C. Paleolithic hunters and fishers who then lived there had grinding stones and sickles of flint, showing that they harvested the seeds of grasses for food. They may not have cultivated them, nor even needed to. Farther north in the Fertile Crescent wild barley and primitive wheat grow today in stands not too unlike planted fields. The rewards of serious agriculture may not have been evident until the rich, moist flood lands of the great Near Eastern rivers were taken over.

From the agricultural and urban centers of the Nile and Asia Minor the art of cultivation spread westward. Along the northern coast of Africa the Phoenicians, mariners and city-builders though they were, developed sound methods of land use and management. So good were they that the Roman Senate made one exception to its decree that all things Carthaginian must be destroyed. The treatise on agriculture by Mago was ordered saved and translated into Latin, where its prescriptions on crop rotation, fertilizers, and so on seem to have been preserved in the writings of Cato, Columella, Agricola, and the Georgics of Virgil.

Trees were no great obstacle in northern Africa, not only because they were scarce, but because the Phoenicians, dealers in and shippers of cedar from Lebanon, had metal for axes as early as 2500 B.C. Whatever the original conditions of plant cover in northern Africa may have been, it became the principal source of cereal foodstuffs for Rome as agriculture declined and population grew in the Italian Peninsula.

In southern Europe it is believed that westward movement was not seriously handicapped by dense forests. Certainly the Mediterranean climate favored an open woodland, whose survivors today are represented by the olive, cork-oak, fig, and laurel. As the Neolithic farmers worked westward from the Fertile Crescent they possessed axes of polished stone and later of bronze. They also had efficient aides in the form of livestock, notably goats that completed and even extended the work of clearing. This function of livestock was well known to pioneers in the wooded lands beyond the Appalachians who used sheep to "clean up the brush" after big trees had been felled.

Plato in an oft-quoted passage records his own observations on the mischief done to soil and water by axe, plow, and grazing on the hills of Greece. It did not take long for the open forests of the Mediterranean lands to be replaced by woody scrub, not unlike the chaparral of California, and known as maquis or garigue.

Fertilizers, rotation, and other safeguards were increasingly necessary to permanent agriculture as the vulnerable soils of heavily forested regions in western Europe were cleared for cultivation. Meanwhile, however, as republic became empire and farms became estates, responsible ownership drifted away from the land and the status of the farm worker changed from yeoman to serf. The admirable care and discipline of rural life began to disintegrate.

Whatever the detailed steps may have been, it is clear that medieval land use and management in Europe was about as bad as it could be. Feudalism, with its scorn for both manual labor and learning, was beautifully adapted to continue the downward course that began in the waning days of Roman greatness. Due to the failure to use fertilizers and legumes in rotation, land was kept in fallow for one or two years out of three. There was seldom enough feed to keep more than a small proportion of livestock over winter. This, plus the lack of preservative means other than smoke and salt, led to the early winter slaughter of all but the most indispensable animals. This traditional butchering time also found the animals in best condition from summer pasture and forage, while the cool days helped delay spoilage of the meat.

Thus the year's end provided food for the traditional feasts of pagan and Christian times, while the end of winter frequently meant hard going, with food supplies at their lowest. A good case can be made for considering Lenten restrictions as virtue arising from necessity. Like bear and squirrel, our forefathers probably emerged from the long night of winter lean, hungry, and ready to go, whether with prayer or curse.

As the Middle Ages gradually gave birth to the awakening of the fifteenth and sixteenth centuries with the invention of printing, improvement in navigation and other arts, the discovery of America and its flood of gold, old ways and restrictions began to yield. Through political and religious change and actual physical movement the oppressed and dissatisfied were able in some measure to escape from their bonds.

Coming to the New World by voyages of incredible hardship, they found themselves transplanted from one forest region to another, different though the plants and animals were. With sweat and steel they took over, to gain fuel, building material, and space. Thus from the start their motives were mixed. The source of what they needed was also their rival for space in which to plant and grow their foodstuffs.

One fact, often overlooked, was destined to be of the utmost importance. The yeomanry and artificer families that settled in bleak New England, like the gentry and their dependents that came to the land known as Virginia, came from a Britain that was still practicing wasteful and inefficient medieval agriculture. The disastrous effects of this tradition can be seen in eroded hills, silted valleys, and abandoned farms, not only near the eastern coast, but in the path of westward migration. The awakening interest which was to make scientific agriculture a fashionable concern among English gentlemen came too late to benefit settlers in the northern and southern colonies. By the time Jefferson and others began to share the new enlightenment, gullying was well advanced and soils in many places were exhausted. In fairness it should be added that neither in New England nor in the south Atlantic states do the soils have great natural fertility.

In contrast the midatlantic colonies, Pennsylvania, Maryland, and Delaware received a strong infusion of settlers from the continent of Europe who brought with them generally sound practices of land use and management. While the exact record is obscure, there had been during the sixteenth and early seventeenth centuries a remarkable flowering of interest in better agriculture in the Netherlands. The reforms that resulted were much like the best practices known to the Romans. Did these diffuse out from monastic centers where they had been observed in use, or were they uncovered in classical literature? How much credit is due to the burgeoning universities, early fountains of science? How much to the insistence on assured returns by thrifty Dutch merchants who may have become landowners?

Doubtless all of these conditions were involved to some degree. At any rate, their influence spread over northern Europe, refining the best of traditional peasant lore from Scandinavia to Switzerland but making slow progress where feudalism remained strong, as in East Prussia. Unfortunately it did not, as we have said, reach England in time to benefit either the north or south Atlantic regions. Only the middle coastline was helped, thanks to the Swedes, Germans, and other continentals who settled there.

Visiting northwestern Europe today, one sees thrifty management and operation of the land, to be sure, but a wise allocation of uses as well. The various needs—crops, pasture, woodland, game, recreation, and so on—are recognized and met in spite of the high cost of land. Forestry both private and public is practiced with a skill and intensity unmatched here. One holding in Denmark of two thousand acres of forest employs fifty men year around and more when farm work is light. Some of our national forests would be lucky to have one forester to ten times that area.

Even had a more fortunate tradition with respect to the land been brought over from the British Isles it might have been dissipated by the vastness of the new country and the rapid expansion of industry and commerce. From the 1850's when the center of lumbering was in western New York, this industry has swept along to its present strongholds in Northwest and Southeast. In its wake are farms, towns, and cities which it has helped warm, house, and furnish as well as make room for. But its passing has also left behind millions of acres best suited to the growing of forest, now unproductive, unable in our present economy to sustain the hordes that are swarming off the land and into cities which cannot use, let alone decently absorb them.

chapter sixteen

The New Forest

SO we see modern man, whose ancestors swarmed forth from the forest and out across vast open lands, now funneling back into forests of concrete and steel, the cities of today. The quality which suggests this comparison is not, like the open timbering and delicate tracery of the Gothic cathedral, a matter of aesthetic intent absorbed from woodland beauty at its best. For the forest, like any landscape, can be many things to many men. What we see mirrored in the tall structures and narrow paths of the metropolis are some of the less lovely aspects of deep, dense, and gloomy primeval forest.

We think of shade as always cool and woods as a haven for animal life. One need only be caught in a dense and breathless forest on a hot day looking for game to be disillusioned. True, he will find animals—invertebrate midges and mosquitoes—but not much target material for his camera or gun. The blessings of cool shade and teeming bird and mammal life are to be found where the monotony of heavy forest is broken by the presence of open space. Needless to say, the modern city seldom has much open space.

When the journalist Elmer Peterson assembled his book *Cities Are Abnormal* in 1946, urban problems did not have the high and disturbing visibility that recent violence has given them. This was even true in a measure ten years later when Joseph Spengler wrote in the *Harvard Business Review* that "Population Threatens Prosperity," although that decade saw, for example, a doubling in size of Mexico City. What Spengler demonstrated was that after a city reaches its optimum size, a dimension that varies with conditions, further increase becomes an economic liability instead of an asset.

Quite reasonably, most well-meaning and even expert concern with urban problems focuses on the obvious sore spots—slums, poverty, crime, delinquency, sanitation, health, and central decay. Like the battlefield surgeons of an earlier day, we are inclined to think at once of excision or amputation, cushioned not by opium but by that well-known anodyne, money. I suspect a better approach is to take a hint from the best of modern medical practice, looking past symptoms to the condition of the whole organism and recognizing pain killers for the short-term expedient they are.

No city, not even the stout-walled town of medieval times, is an entity complete in itself. Rather it is part of a total functioning landscape. The use by Neolithic man in Egypt of flint sickles and grinding stones as early as 12000 B.C. had expanded by 8000 B.C. into an agriculture sufficient to support villages in the Near East. Without more reliable and abundant supplies of food than can be had by hunting, fishing, and gathering, no considerable concentrations of people can exist. The city is the child of the farm; too often it seems to be an ungrateful one.

The earliest cities not only owed their beginning to agriculture, but were functionally part of it. As we uncover ruins both in the Old and New World, assemble their artifacts, study their arts and interpret the beginnings of written records, we find good cause to revise our notions of what we have been calling the heathen, barbarian, pagan world, ridden, as we conceive it, by cruel superstition.

That the earliest cities were ceremonial and religious centers is clear enough. That they served *mutatis mutandis,* in a role equivalent to that of a modern Ministry of Agriculture ought to be understood, with a bit of explanation, by the backyard gardener. As I write, many crops, notably tomatoes, have been unseasonably late in many states. The supply of rain, regime of temperature, incidence of pests, and generosity of the soil vary in ways not easy to understand and often impossible to foresee. Even in our technologic age horticulture and farming are conceded to be full of hazards.

Consequently the modern farmer (and indeed the business, professional, and industrial man) does precisely what men have always done: he uses the knowledge he has so far as it will go and entrusts the rest to luck, or prayer. Some of the knowledge basic to farming came early, especially that dealing with the seasons and the simple physical principles needed to control irrigation water and tool design.

To get, refine, and preserve such knowledge, even the most elementary kind, takes time and energy only to be had by release from manual labor. This release which we call leisure was one of the first gifts of crude agriculture, nor was it grudgingly bestowed. I have seen a farm boy sent out of the cornfield on a cold December day lest he ruin his hands by husking and be unable to fiddle for the neighborhood at night, and another exempted from physical labor so he could help with tax returns.

The hunter, now graduated into farmer, had already been accustomed to thinking of unseen but personified forces as responsible for the uncertainties of his livelihood. More than ever he was glad to leave the transactions with these unknown powers to professionals, the more so as they began to accumulate a considerable amount of reliable knowledge. After all, if one has a nucleus of information he can do fairly well by random choice on a true-false test. There were sound practical reasons for the organization of early cities around priesthoods and their temples—precursors of our modern institutes, laboratories, and multiversities.

This fairly straightforward pattern of life generally became complicated if not corrupted by military and commercial developments, to say nothing of human cussedness and lust for power as cities grew in size and in economic and political control of the tributary landscape. With almost fatalistic regularity the great city-centered empires have, like the life of the individual, come to an end. Their postmortems are as varied as the predilections of the explainer. One of the most durable cultures, despite many serious setbacks, has been that of the Chinese. Until swamped by modern technology, it ranked the farmer only below the scholar, with merchant and soldier trailing in that order.

Since the city is a product of the rural landscape and cannot survive without it even now, there may be something to gain by looking at the larger landscape, working inward towards the trouble spots.

Until the 1870's—a decade of disaster to aboriginal forests, wildlife, and men—urban population was less than half of the total in the United

States. Between that decade and 1930, rural population dropped from 50 percent to 30 percent and now stands at something like 7 percent. One farm worker now produces food enough for forty people. Change is moving faster and faster as shown by an increase of 50 percent in the productivity of a single farm worker within the last ten years.

To say this change is due to our clever application of scientific knowledge is true only in part. Work, no matter how efficient the machine, requires energy. Only a couple of generations ago that energy was the muscle power of man and beast, filtered from the sun through crop plants. Today it represents the sunshine from millions of years back, preserved in fossil form as coal, oil, and gas, increasingly fed to farm and factory through internal combustion engines.

While the effect of power machinery on rural life started with the Industrial Revolution, supplanting cottage workshops and drawing labor to factories, the big speedup began with the First World War. The croplands of western Europe became battlefields, and breadstuffs a munition. Wheat was grown wherever it could be, but the premium for low cost mass production went to level or gently rolling semiarid land where dry farming could be carried on with big machinery on big acreages. When the high wartime prices for wheat dropped, the small farmer could no longer compete with these new "factories in the fields," and for him the great depression began in 1920, nearly ten years before it hit the rest of the nation. Meanwhile, he hung on as best he could and during the 1930's offered food and shelter to unemployed kinfolk who came back from idle urban factories. It was now the time, thanks to prolonged drought, for the mechanized wheat grower in the dry plains to encounter trouble.

However, a new pattern had been set, giving advantage to large, highly mechanized and heavily capitalized farming. World War II and its Korean aftermath pushed it into full swing. A second period of overproduction, countered by acreage restriction instead of market control, plus payment for retiring land from production, gave further leverage to the large, well-financed operator. To clinch the urban-industrial-financial pattern now imposed on the rural landscape, farm machinery was becoming more powerful and more costly as competitive urban wages increased—for those lucky enough to get urban employment.

Not only did the number of farm workers drop from 30 percent of our population in 1920 to 7 percent in the 1960's, but between 1940 and 1963 the number of farms decreased from 6,096,799 to 3,703,894 while those larger than a thousand acres increased by 35,678. Expressive as these figures are, they tell only part of the story. During the late 1940's I visited a rich cotton-growing area. The tiny cabins of the workers were hedged in by plowed and planted cotton fields. There were no gardens, no cows, no poultry, or pigs. Dependence upon field wages was absolute. Trials were being made of cotton picking machinery. In the words of one planter, "We're fixing to mechanize. Cotton is selling around 30 and we're doing all right. But we plan to make money if she drops to 12." In response to a query as to what would happen to the workers and their families, came the cool reply, "We'll let folks worry about them in Cleveland and Detroit." Nothing if not a prescient statement, as recent troubles prove!

Whether or not the flood of Puerto Rican Americans was precipitated by Spanish-speaking politicians who saw the chance for cheap and plentiful votes, these immigrants to the city, like southern field hands, were poorly equipped to take an effective part in urban life. So too were the unemployed coal miners of Appalachia, displaced by massive strip-mining machinery. Many of these last have remained where they were, on relief, which in one county accounts for 80 percent of its residents.

As to the smaller, once prosperous, family farms that have been absorbed into large units in the corn and wheat belts, the former owners and tenants have either retired or—by virtue of favorable background—found productive employment in town and city. Some of the more thrifty have kept a foot on the earth by living on small acreages, growing much that they need in their spare time from factory, shop, or office work. It is the massive shift of long underprivileged (as we call them) from land to city that has created an intolerable problem. These millions are without role or niche.

On the assumption that each new recruit to a city is a new customer and possibly a new taxpayer and that growth in numbers is the mark of urban vitality, the cult of Boosterism has come to be the dominant faith among Chambers of Commerce. Not much expertise is needed, if one has the patience to look into the finances of rapidly growing cities, to uncover the fallacies of this doctrine. More professionally, as Joseph Spengler has shown, cities tend to have an optimum size beyond which growth represents a liability instead of an asset. Quite apart from the economics involved, the sociologist viewing the facts of delinquency, educational breakdown, environmental disorder, and general frustration should concede that optimum size has often been exceeded.

Whether or not one agrees with the persuasive view of Professor and Mrs. Lincoln Day in their book *Too Many Americans,* he would be hard put to deny that our population is badly distributed in terms of what life should be in a humane and civilized society. Unless urban planning and renewal can create genuine niches and roles for what now amounts to an undigested bolus of humanity, which looks doubtful, no amount of spectacular new building will help. The only answer would seem to lie in redistributing people to new locations where ample space gives a better chance to develop decent living conditions and economic opportunity.

Can this be done without resorting to the kind of authoritarianism we used more than a century ago in herding Wyandots, Creeks, and other Indians, dispossessed of their own fair and fertile lands? Can it be more realistic in building up functional communities than some of the well-meant relocation schemes of thirty years ago, to say nothing of Indian reservations or refugee camps in other lands today?

The city is a physical system as well as a social milieu. These two aspects cannot be dealt with separately for they are intimately interwoven. Even human society itself, however plastic it may seem in response to different cultures and diverse conditions, is a physical system. (This is not to say that it is, as some insist, a *mere* physical system.) It consists of dynamic units within a finite space. As such it responds—like gas molecules within a flask—to increase of numbers within a given space by increased pressure and diminished freedom of movement.

Further, if energy is added to the system, pressure is further increased and freedom further restricted. In technical language, the mean free path of each particle is decreased and the number of collisions between units rises proportionately. These conditions come about when a flask of gas is heated or when a human community finds that fossil fuel can be used to put its individual members on wheels.

Actually a good case can be made for the idea that an excess of available energy is bound to disrupt the system receiving it. Professor V. R. Damerell of Cleveland uses the example of a drop of water on a hot stove. At a very different level, we have already discussed the disastrous effect of abundance on the lemmings and their predators.

Although an army must, as Napoleon said, march on its belly, it needs many things besides food to keep it going. The city exploits the country that surrounds it, as the army lives on the country through which it moves. New York and Philadelphia reach far north for water, Los Angeles some two hundred miles to the east. These and other American cities draw their crude oil for heating and power from across the oceans, their refined automobile fuel from within the nation where it yields higher profits to the producers. Since California orchards have been so largely sacrificed for "development," that state brings in its orange juice from Florida. Bales of nylon stockings come through the Panama Canal to be finished more profitably on the West Coast. A quick inventory of any urban breakfast table is a good lesson in geography.

But at the same time, the city also transforms, just as any living community does when it manufactures and deploys the stuff that life is made of. In forest and meadow this stuff and the energy stored in it are on loan to the individual organisms during their life span. In return, their activities tend to keep the system in repair and perpetuate it. Most important, these materials continue to be recycled through air and earth for the use of successive generations. Evolution brings its changes and so do the inevitable fluctuations of environment. Species become extinct, but others take their place. Climates shift and earth forms become modified, but life goes on, adjusting itself to new conditions, whether rigorous or genial.

Here we have the model upon which any hope of reasonable permanence of the human adventure must be patterned. Against this model we must measure the dynamics of our present urbanized, technological civilization.

If one considers the flow of energy and materials created by the modern city, he is reminded of a vortex sucking in from every possible source all that comes within its whirling, centripetal reach. What is drawn into a vortex, be it a kitchen drain or an ocean whirlpool, must go somewhere. The urban vortex, having finished with its food, fuel, raw materials, and myriad artifacts, whirls what is left into the surrounding air, earth, and waters. Despite the quite respectable efforts of those who can make a profit from reclaiming junk and other wastes, the bulk of it remains unused and unusable, a loss at best, a nuisance or even a source of danger at worst.

Compounding this extravagance is that grisly companion of the modern city: organized, industrialized, highly technological, modern warfare. Two of these great conflicts have eaten away and dissipated mountains of rich metallic ores, to say nothing of seas of liquid fuel which, though abundant, is still finite in amount and vital for peaceful purposes. The cost in human lives and tragedy belongs in another ledger.

I have often tried, without success, to find a pattern in nature resembling that of our urbanized civilization—not as it might be—but as it is now. Destruction, concentration, dissipation, and extinction do exist in nature. But these seem to be balanced and compensated for by a generally constructive trend of organization and economy in the recycling of material and deploying of energy. Thus far, unless I am completely wrong, the trend of man's activity is to lower, rather than maintain or enhance, the capacity of environment to sustain him in the long run.

Many view the solution as primarily a matter of economics and applied science. It is, of course, both and on a stupendous scale. In one city which has helped make Lake Erie a cesspool, the first step is known to be the separation of sanitary and storm sewers. To accomplish this will cost eighty million dollars—an amount beyond the present dreams of this city, troubled as it is by riot and chronic crime. Yet one month's cost of a remote war now going on would, if my calculations are correct, revamp the sewers of twenty such cities. It is time for a hard look at priorities.

Whatever success we may have in improving the situation created by crowding ourselves into the new forests of steel and concrete must come from a far more general understanding of man as a part of the world of nature than we now have. The products of this kind of knowledge cannot be sold over the counter like new chemical compounds or mechanisms based on physical principles, nor does it contribute to military might. It holds no sensational promises, no prospects of tailoring new breeds of men by getting at the biochemistry of genes and brains.

There are hopeful signs that science will not continue to be cherished—or despised—as the New Sorcery. And there is hope, too, that a new generation of citizens will be given a proper appreciation of science as a source of perspective rather than of expedients.

Man, who emerged from his ancestral forests into a long day in the open sun only to return to shadows of his own creation, now has the chance to emerge again, providing he does not ignore the lessons of his long past in making use of his new knowledge.

Index